Manufacturing:

Strategy for Growth and Change

About the Author

Thomas A. Faulhaber is a partner in the management engineering consulting firm of Ganteaume & McMullen. He is a graduate of Massachusetts Institute of Technology and received his M.B.A. degree from Harvard University.

A registered professional engineer in Massachusetts and 21 other states, Mr. Faulhaber was awarded the Daniel W. Mead Prize by the American Society of Civil Engineers in 1963.

Currently Mr. Faulhaber lectures on industrial management at Northeastern University's Graduate School of Engineering. He is a member of the American Institute of Industrial Engineers, the American Society of Civil Engineers, the Boston Society of Civil Engineers, the National Association of Manufacturers (Area Industrial Problems Committee), the National Society of Professional Engineers, and Tau Beta Pi.

Mr. Faulhaber has contributed to a number of engineering and industrial journals. His articles have appeared in *American Engineer*, *Baker's Weekly*, *Baking Industry*, *Consulting Engineer*, *Food Engineering*, and *Industry*.

Manufacturing: Strategy for Growth and Change

By

THOMAS A. FAULHABER

AMERICAN MANAGEMENT ASSOCIATION

Preface

If you haven't the strength to impose your own terms upon life, you must accept the terms it offers you.

—T. S. Eliot

THE ERA OF UNCERTAIN PEACE and police-action military engagements following the end of World War II has witnessed profound social and economic realignments throughout the world. Manufacturing industries exist in an environment in which few of the generalizations of the past are valid. The role of manufacturing has been redefined; the manufacturing function is performed within a new set of constraints and often is expected to meet unprecedented objectives.

Sometime before the 1940's, economists and industrial managers began to recognize that we had overcome most of the more basic production problems—that making things was becoming a much smaller problem than selling things. As our mass manufacturing capabilities and technology enabled us to manufacture products of high quality in vast quantities and interesting variety, we began to encounter the problems of distributing and of creating sound and sustained consumer demand for the profusion of products from our factories. In response to this challenge, industrial management has acknowledged and elevated the marketing function, frequently to a point of paramount importance, within an industrial organization. The past two decades have seen many of our most notable manufacturing corporations become market-oriented—thus frequently as-

5

suming a radically different stance from that envisioned by their founders.

The unparalleled economic stability and prosperity of the period since 1945 have resulted in extraordinary opportunities for corporate growth and in highly complex competitive relationships between industrial units. In response to this combination of factors, industrial management has begun to perceive the need for and the importance of strategic planning. Strategy formulation is not new to the manufacturing industries. But the management process of consciously developing and defining—in adequate detail—the strategy of a total corporation has not been common prior to the present decade. The ultra-high-tension atmosphere in which today's industrial enterprises operate requires that management plan its future consciously, aggressively, and strategically; the alternative is likely to be corporate impotence, if not annihilation.

A third trend to be noted is that, while the manufacturing industries are becoming market-oriented and the more perceptive managements are now engaged in strategic planning, the manufacturing function has been undergoing revolutionary changes. Both product and production technology have experienced a generation of ferment. Automation is no longer a slogan but a routine standard of electromechanical design. Manufacturing activities are being monitored, adjusted, and directed by advanced and highly automatic operational control systems. Today, our manufacturing industries are characterized by high production rates, enhanced flexibility of output, and exceptional standards of product quality and reliability —all coupled with responsive cost control capabilities that were only speculations 20 years ago.

Without making an exhaustive analysis of the industrial trends of the past two decades, one may conclude that management awareness and action in the conjunctive areas of marketing and corporate strategy have been dramatically effective; perhaps in consequence, management's focus upon the operational-mechanical aspects of manufacturing has commonly resulted in blurring or ignoring the strategic implications of the manufacturing function. Corporate strategy and marketing strategy usually and quite properly are synonymous; the concept of a manufacturing strategy is not familiar except as a secondary component of corporate strategy. Frequently, the strategic planning process is based upon the notion "If we can sell it, we can make it." Although this may be a workable orientation in certain situations, in many others it results in the ineffective acquisition, utilization, and disposition of a corporation's always limited resources.

This book seeks to identify and explore those aspects of manufacturing strategy that are primary vectors in the formulation of a total corporate strategy. It seeks to develop a frame of reference that will encourage the establishment of superior manufacturing objectives derived from the formulation of a kinetic strategy of manufacturing —a strategy of growth and change. It recognizes the interdependency of manufacturing decisions and total corporate strategy, and emphasizes the contributions to be made by manufacturing management to the formulation and implementation of an effective strategy.

It is hoped that this book will be bifocal. First, it raises questions concerning a corporation's manufacturing activities that the directors should ask continually and answer dispassionately. Second, it investigates the questions—even when not asked—which operating management should identify and resolve convincingly for the directors and the shareholders in an effort to develop a superior manufacturing strategy that energizes and coincides with the total strategy of the enterprise.

In the United States, "value added by manufacture" represents about one-third of our gross national product—and similar statistics are typical of other industrial nations. This manufacturing capability is the foundation of our national wealth and strength, of our historically high and stable levels of employment, and of our increasing leisure to fulfill the noblest human aspirations and potentialities. The manufacturing capability and expanding technology of each industrial unit—collectively, one-third of our national productivity —is dependent upon the conscious formulation of a kinetic strategy for growth and change.

The purpose of this book is to state cogently and clearly the strategic questions of manufacturing and to examine some of the ways in which these questions can be answered usefully. This work will be well rewarded if it helps industrial management, through an enhanced understanding of the strategic dimensions of its manufacturing activities, to formulate creative corporate strategies.

Acknowledgments

THE MOST LUMINOUS intellectual reward a writer may earn is an enhanced understanding of the principles and complexities within his area of inquiry. Humility, however, is an inevitable moral reward. Upon undertaking this investigation, I became swiftly aware of the limitations of my knowledge and experience, of the vanity and often fallacy of the few insights I had surmised to be valid and even unique, and of the prodigious debt I already owed to others. The sources from which these efforts have been nourished—indeed, the cultural heritage from which each of us draws continually—are incalculable.

Acknowledging only a few of the most obvious and important contributions to this work, I want to begin with the exceptional role of my parents. They offered unending opportunities for growth and an indulgent freedom for exploration. Few men are endowed with a father who is an industrial manager of notable achievement and who is so willing to share instructively his aspirations, accomplishments, and perception of the industrial process.

In developing this book, I was fortunate to be able to examine and test my concepts and understanding of both the process and practice of manufacturing strategy with a select group of men of industrial eminence. Each of these men, even though burdened with extensive responsibilities, was gracious in making the time available for our discussions about the book; in a number of cases, this invaluable dialogue necessitated several meetings and continual correspondence. Among those who were most generous and constructive, I wish to acknowledge the special help of E. Pennell Brooks, of the Alfred P. Sloan School of Management, Massachusetts Institute of Technology; Melvin J. Gilbert, of The Great Atlantic and Pacific

9

Tea Company; Gordon Grand, of Olin Mathieson Chemical Corporation; Semon E. Knudson, of General Motors Corporation; Stanley de J. Osborne, of Lazard Freres & Co.; Thomas L. Phillips, of Raytheon Company; and Vincent C. Ziegler, of The Gillette Company. Although their ideas, corrections, and amiable points of disagreement have been uniquely important, it is to be emphasized that unanimous concurrence was neither secured nor expected on all of the concepts presented in this book, and that only I can accept responsibility for its interpretations of facts and trends and for its conclusions.

A primary source of guidance and assistance has been the clients with whom I have worked so closely in my consulting practice. This is where theory must be transformed into superior performance, where grand designs must lead to measurable achievement, and where intellectual elegance is meaningful only in terms of strategic effectiveness. Here my partner, H. C. Thomas, and colleagues in our organization have played an inestimable role for many years; my special thanks are extended to Anna Strobel for her thoughtful reading and critique of the manuscript in its several versions. I also want to acknowledge the incisive questioning of my teaching associates as well as the refreshing and frequently disturbing ideas offered by a number of my graduate students, with whom it is always gratifying to work.

Finally, no acknowledgment can express adequately the help of my family. My wife's unflagging interest and ingenuous questions may constitute my most sobering gift. Tireless good humor, encouragement, and unbounding understanding are only her most apparent contributions to the creation of this book.

THOMAS A. FAULHABER

Contents

I

Function

There is nothing permanent except change.
—Heraclitus

Observe always that everything is the result of a change, and get used to thinking that there is nothing Nature loves so well as to change existing forms and to make new ones like them.
—Marcus Aurelius Antoninus

THE 20TH CENTURY is called "the century of change." But even the casual student of history knows that every era in the past has been a period of change. The longevity of a few monolithic dynasties is deceptive; the thoughtful study of any epoch reveals that extensive and penetrating change has affected the lives of most peoples throughout history. Change may have come about through military invasion, religious ferment, or the processes of commerce, but continuing and usually pervasive change has been the one constant of history. History, in fact, is the story of change.

Today we are preoccupied with change. The speaker or author who fails to admonish his audience about the implications of the accelerating rate of change, or the industrial leader who does not caution his associates and subordinates about the dangers of ignoring change, not only is out of date but also is likely to be deficient

in socio-economic awareness and responsibility. *Change* is a plati-
tude—a fashionable catchword, often reinforced with apocalyptic
adjectives, to describe a supposedly unique and important development of contemporary history.

It is true, of course, that we live in an era of change. To ignore or
deny the frequency and magnitude of the changes witnessed by our
generation would be fatuous; however, it would be equally debilitating to exaggerate the influence of change on our lives. To be understood and exploited constructively, change must be viewed in
historical perspective; that is, change must be comprehended as the
kinetic continuity of history. In accepting its constancy throughout
history, what are the aspects of change today that strike us as new
and perhaps as threatening?

First, the presence of many factors affecting virtually every aspect
of our lives results in a *rate of change* that matches, if it does not
exceed, that experienced during any era in the past. At random, the
identification of a few of these factors might include the ever widen-
ing displacement of myth, magic, and ritual by the scientific analysis
and interpretation of our environment; the achievement of almost
universal literacy in the more advanced nations and of improving
literacy levels in the less developed areas of the world; the rapidly
rising standards of living and aspirations in life throughout the
world; and the conscious and munificently funded research programs
(governmental as well as industrial), probing almost every facet of
our lives, that have suddenly become commonplace—especially in
the United States and in a few other nations in the West. Abundant
evidence supports the statement that the 20th century is indeed a
century of change, and that in many respects our present and foreseeable rate of change appears to be unprecedentedly rapid and
universal.

Second, not only are our lives immersed in an environment of
change, but also our extraordinary communications media make us
more immediately aware of change than ever before. Both the general and specialized news media subsist on change. Yet while
acknowledging the frequency and magnitude of current change, we
cannot deny that the appearance or recognition of truly significant
change is comparatively rare. Consequently, the news media must
constantly manufacture news heralding novelty and mere cleverness
as change and all too frequently must present fabricated change in

,lace of the more elusive achievements and developments that are destined to shape our future. The shrill, incessant outpourings from most of our communications media easily lead one to believe that change is occurring at a breathless, terrifying, and overwhelming rate. This is good entertainment. On the other hand, too often the almost unlimited capabilities of our communications media engulf the significant in the irrelevant; mislead the gullible, less thoughtful observer; and produce an audience that is shocked, bored, or merely confused rather than enlightened. Overstating the dimensions and implications of change has tended to blur our perception of this vital contemporary phenomenon rather than to sharpen our understanding of it.

COMMUNICATIONS AND CHANGE

We live in an exciting kaleidoscopic environment of change. Very likely, much of the vitality of this environment is derived from our newfound awareness of change. In the past, a local flour mill might have operated for several generations at the same location with essentially the same capital equipment, producing but one mix of products, serving the same market, meeting the same—limited— competition, and pursuing the same owner-manager objectives. All this time change, undetected by the miller, was affecting one, two, or perhaps all of these factors. Then suddenly, when it was too late, the cumulative results of change would overwhelm the complacent miller. Any steps he might now take to accommodate his milling activity to the dramatically new circumstances would be futile, and the operation would wither quickly.

Today, enhanced economic as well as social literacy, coupled with improved communications, has made us aware of and continually sensitive to change. The managements of the worldwide and even regional milling companies now exhibit a relatively high level of global awareness of technological improvements, of changing transportation patterns, of comparative wage rates and labor productivity, of the costs and advantages of existing and pending taxation policies, of crop forecasts and yield trends, of new dietary preferences and product developments, and of a multitude of other factors affecting the industry and the relationships of their operations to the industry.

This is, then, the century of accelerating change century of vastly improved communications. Desp. abuses of our communications media, it is now possible to change in ways that, until recently, were nonexistent. While contemporary rate of change may exceed that experienced at any time in the past, our awareness of and sensitivity to change and the capability of knowing about change in virtually any area of the world at almost the instant of its occurrence are the aspects of change today that rank it as a new and frequently threatening phenomenon. A threatening phenomenon? Yes, threatening, because competitors within an industry or to an industry, international competitors, and even national rivals all have access to the same capabilities. Today, change is rarely the outgrowth of mysterious or remote socio-economic developments; it is the product of intelligence and conscious action. Change is manufactured; the principal product of the viable manufacturer is change.

The metals markets offer a popular illustration of continually changing competitive alignments. In 1966, for example, approximately 16 percent of the output of the aluminum industry was earmarked for communications and electrical end uses—a field formerly dominated by copper. In the 1950's, the long-distance, high-tension transmission and distribution cable market—another former province of copper—was almost completely delivered to aluminum. Despite poorer soldering qualities and greater bulk (due to lower conductivity—63 percent that of copper), more efficient thinner insulations now permit aluminum to compete effectively for low-voltage distribution circuits, electric machinery, and other fine-wire applications.

The Aluminum Company of America has developed a solid aluminum magnet strip for transformer windings that appears to offer advantages comparable to copper. Texas Instruments Incorporated has achieved commercial production of a copper-clad aluminum wire employing only 10 percent as much copper as solid copper wire and costing 30 percent less; this product promises innumerable applications in electronics (only the copper surface of the wire is used for high frequency electronic transmissions) as well as for automotive battery cables and coaxial cable for community television antennae.

Although persistently in short supply, copper has also been the beneficiary of product development, which has resulted in many new

and imaginative product applications—such as copper-clad aluminum curtain wall panels that offer expanded architectural uses.
Similarly, nickel, the traditional material for high-resistance con-
ductors for electric heating (in electric blankets and toasters, for
instance), must compete with Kanthal—an iron-based alloy con-
taining no nickel—that has been the dominant material for resist-
ance wiring in Europe since the 1920's and has now become a major
material for these applications in the United States. Another competitive realignment has been initiated by the United States Steel
Corporation, which derives twin benefits from producing steel foils
in commercial widths in gauges as fine as 0.001 inches: the ability
to compete in the metal foils market formerly dominated by aluminum and tin and the opportunity to enter into new market areas.

OBSOLESCENCE AND CHANGE

Not only does the manufacturer live and work in an environment
of change, but he is also a principal contributor of change to our
total environment. Products are in a state of continuous and deliberate evolution—frequently, of revolution. In most industries, manufacturing technology is advancing so rapidly that the methods and
machines of production are obsolete and uncompetitive—sometimes,
that is, within a span of only two or three years, more often
within six to ten years. Substantial annual revisions of both the
channels and the physical methods of distribution are widespread;
distribution technology exerts a primary influence on product configuration and end use. Even corporate objectives are continually
being redefined to accommodate new environmental constraints and
opportunities. The universal and pervasive presence of change is
usually a dominant parameter of a manufacturing activity.

Although change may be an important influence upon any activity,
at least one unique consideration emphasizes its special importance
to the manufacturer. Contemporary manufacturing activities—
which often exhibit high levels of mechanization or automation
—inevitably require comparatively large fixed capital investments.
In most manufacturing companies capital is used principally for
plant, equipment, and related facilities of production. The physical
nature of most of these assets usually is rather inflexible; once they

are acquired, it may not be possible to transform them economically to meet the unanticipated marketing and manufacturing demands of the future. The manufacturer is confronted with the dilemma of having to make very large investments in manufacturing facilities to remain competitive, knowing that the uncertainties of the future could render these facilities partially or even totally obsolete overnight; quite possibly, this could result in unacceptable losses to the shareholders of the enterprise.

Either intuitive or explicit models of the future must be constructed by every manager to make coherent decisions affecting the future of the enterprise. The futurity of present decisions is important in any economic activity; to the manufacturer, it may be of paramount importance for two reasons. First, the magnitude of capital investments for manufacturing facilities often exceeds that of capital investments required for all other functions. And, second, to contribute a satisfactory profit, manufacturing facilities usually must be employed productively for fairly long periods of time—at least a few years in some situations and many years or decades in others. Thus the outlook for the manufacturer's present decisions is appreciably more sensitive to situational changes than is the outlook for decisions affecting other functional areas. (This could provide the behavioral scientist with a tidy explanation for the generic conservatism of manufacturers.)

DEFINITION AND SCOPE

To avoid confusion or misunderstanding, it may be helpful to define the sense in which we use the word "manufacturing." For purposes of this discussion, our definition is rather loose: Manufacturing is an economic function concerned with making things. "Things" implies that the manufacturing function results in some physical output: for example, washing machines, electrical energy, or space-vehicle propulsion units. "Making" suggests that parts are combined, that shape is imparted to material, or that matter is transformed to bring something identifiably different into existence. For example, selected electronic components are made (assembled) into a printed circuit, steel blanks are made (machined) into turbine vanes, or free air is made (reduced) into liquid nitrogen and liquid oxygen.

Manufacturing can also be defined as "material transformation";

to manufacture is to transform matter. An aluminum reduction plant, a sugar refinery, a paper mill, a building construction project, and an automobile assembly plant are all manufacturing activities concerned with *transforming* certain raw materials from one form into some other form of greater utility and value to society. Our definition of manufacturing is sufficiently broad to encompass mining and other extractive activities, although this may be at variance with common usage and with the traditional patterns of industrial organization.

Certain activities, such as packaging and physical distribution, may be included as a part of the manufacturing function in many industrial organizations. Although this is, in many instances, a logical and advantageous relationship of functional responsibilities, packaging and physical distribution do not fall within our general definition of manufacturing. A company engaged solely in packaging and physical distribution is not truly engaged in manufacturing inasmuch as it is not making things (even though an interesting argument may be developed that it is making things more salable). However, the manufacturing function in which packaging and physical distribution are separate activities and responsibilities is quite common. Thus this discussion requires not a rigorous definition but simply an acceptance of broad limits upon the types of activities to be designated as manufacturing.

Manufacturing is only one of several functional areas within an industrial organization. There are various concepts of management organization but, at its most rudimentary, organization includes three primary functions: manufacturing (making things), marketing (selling things), and finance (securing and managing money). These primary functions must be coordinated by a general manager, who today usually is assisted by myriad specialists—engineering, research, legal, accounting, and management information staffs.

Today, as product- or task-oriented entities assume the contemporary role of operational management, manufacturing—and the other traditional functions—may not direct operations but will provide, support, and administer the manufacturing resources required by each operations center. Manufacturing and the other functional activities are interdependent; one function is not by definition superior to or more important than some other function. Although this discussion is focused upon the manufacturing function, it is emphasized that a manufacturing activity can seldom be evaluated in a vacuum. A manufacturing strategy is meaningful only as one of the dominant vectors, or guiding forces, of a total corporate strategy. Viewed in this perspective, on the other hand, a manufacturing strategy is separable and whole in somewhat the same sense as naval and air strategy are related to a total national, or politico-military, strategy.

The Manufacturing Option

Manufacturing is the only primary functional activity that may be optional. This attribute of the manufacturing function is commonly ignored; yet it cannot be overemphasized. Whether or not they are so designated, every enterprise must have at least a vestige of a marketing function and of a finance function. Many large and notably healthy industrial organizations, on the other hand, are not engaged in manufacturing; that is, they are not making things. Thus the manufacturing function is permeated with questions and choices without parallel in the other functional areas; an awareness of the presence of these questions and choices is the first step in the development of a manufacturing strategy.

Excluding the television segment of its activities, United Artists Corporation (acquired by Transamerica Corporation in 1967) is the largest and by almost every standard the most successful motion picture producer-distributor for movie theaters; yet it does not make motion pictures. Without owning a single studio or engaging in any of the traditional activities of cinematic production, United Artists has surpassed all other film companies—including the hereditary industry leader, Metro-Goldwyn-Mayer, Inc. Although its worldwide revenues from film rentals and related items totaled $169.1 million in 1966, fixed assets less depreciation were under $1.6 million—or less than 0.8 percent of total corporate assets—and these fixed assets included virtually no production facilities. United Artists Corporation finances specific films of carefully selected independent producers which it distributes and promotes through its global sales organization. The independent producers retain artistic freedom; usually engage the director, writers, cast, production crews, and supporting personnel; and manage the production of the picture; United Artists exercises effective on-location financial control during the shooting of each film. Recognizing the optional nature of manufacturing, the strategy of United Artists is to dispense with this formerly in-house function completely. It underwrites the productions of independent producers and concentrates its efforts in those areas where it has unquestioned superiority—the identification of significant public and film-making trends, the selection of outstanding script-talent-producer combinations, and the marketing and managerial acumen to merchandise these productions throughout the world with maximum effectiveness.

Not only the manufacturing function but also the depth and breadth of manufacturing are optional. Manufacturing may include one or two simple operations or assemblies, or it may include many complex operations or assemblies. For example, a company engaged in the surface-coating business does not necessarily have to manufacture its own product; it can restrict its activities to distribution (possibly including packaging) and marketing, and the manufacturing function can be performed by others under contract. However, if the company has elected to manufacture its own product, it is faced with the option of defining the extent of its manufacturing function. Management may elect one of three options: to purchase all components from others and engage only in the formulation and blending of its products; to manufacture its own pigments, vehicles, and stabilizers as well as blending its products; or to fulfill all of these functions plus manufacturing its own containers and the accessory equipment for the application of its surface coatings. Depending upon which of these various options is chosen, quite different manufacturing strategies obviously would be pursued.

It is interesting to observe, however, that a so-called total manufacturing capability is virtually unknown. Regardless of how extensively the manufacturing function is integrated, the manufacturer usually is dependent upon other manufacturers for certain requirements. The major automobile companies are often considered to be highly integrated manufacturers, for example, yet this industrial group supports large satellite industries of parts producers and subassembly suppliers and comprises important purchasers of primary metals, rubber, plastic, glass, and electrical components. Thus even the largest and most fully integrated enterprises are continually confronted by options that affect the depth and breadth of their manufacturing functions.

COMPETITIVE ROLE AND PROFITABILITY

It is also interesting to observe that the manufacturing function fulfills different roles in different industries and even for different companies. In certain cases, the manufacturing function may be a central—perhaps an essential—activity. It is difficult, for instance, to envision a major steel company lacking its own basic oxygen furnaces, casting facilities, and rolling mills. (Of course, even the major steel companies have the option of deciding how far backward to integrate into ore and coal mining and coke production and how far forward to integrate into finishing, fabrication, and construction.) In other cases, the manufacturing function may be an ancillary activity. The mass merchandisers and large retailing chains need not, by definition, engage in manufacturing, nor is the manufacturing function likely to become the dominant or an indispensable activity for these enterprises. The role of the manufacturing function may be partially defined by the industry as well as by the company's strategic position within its industry.

Sears, Roebuck and Co. has long been noted for its participation in manufacturing operations and its ownership or investment in merchandise suppliers. Sears has always insisted that its manufacturing operations provide a source of supply superior to any other alternative; has assiduously avoided becoming a holding company or maintaining an equity position in a supplier primarily for investment purposes; and is continually evaluating, adding to, and divesting itself of manufacturing activities.

Over the years, Sears acquired a minority interest in 17 small apparel suppliers and recently joined the controlling shareholders in consolidating these factories into the Kellwood Company; nevertheless, Kellwood furnishes only a modest percentage of Sears' total apparel requirements. Warwick Electronics, Inc., was acquired by Sears to secure an assured source of supply of home electronics equipment; in 1966, a controlling interest in this company was sold to the Whirlpool Corporation after it was determined that the latter would provide the management to operate it competently. Warwick, however, continues to manufacture Sears' home electronics products. The Kenmore and Coldspot brands of appliances also are manufactured by Whirlpool. Sears now owns a mere 4 percent interest in Whirlpool yet continues to purchase approximately 65 percent of its output. Although Sears has investments in substantial manufacturing enterprises, it is essential to note that its annual merchandise requirements are fulfilled by 12,000 to 15,000 independent suppliers. Its own factories seldom supply more than a small proportion of its total needs.

A manufacturing capability may be the primary competitive strength of many companies. Frequently, but not always, efficient high-volume (often automated) manufacturing operations provide a powerful competitive advantage to the largest companies in each industry. A specialized, not easily duplicated, manufacturing technology may be a substantial competitive factor for other companies. In many instances, the competitive advantages of a manufacturing capability may be negligible. A broad manufacturing capability appears to be a competitive necessity for a producer of electric motors and machinery; on the other hand, many producers of electric and electronic control systems exhibit rather limited manufacturing capabilities. The depth and breadth of the manufacturing function may be influenced by its measurable competitive advantage to the company and by the competitive structure of the industry.

The physical characteristic of the manufacturing function is the generation of things rather than services. A printing company is a manufacturer; a publishing company is not necessarily a manufacturer, unless it has selected the option of maintaining a printing capability. The printer generates products, while the publisher provides a service.

Of course, it may be essential or desirable to complement the manufacturing function with an extensive service activity. Installation supervision, operator training, management orientation, preventive maintenance and repair are representative services that frequently may be major elements in a total manufacturing system. Examples of outstanding manufacturers whose market acceptance and success have been derived from strong service support rather than any objective product superiority are well known.

Our definition of manufacturing is that it is an economic function concerned with making things. At the same time, manufacturing must be defined as a functional activity concerned with achieving some specific, identifiable, and measurable economic advantage. Economic advantage presumes, in one way or another, the generation of profits or an enhanced return on the total marginal investment in the manufacturing activity. To be credible, this economic advantage must be quantified. "But we have always made this product," "But this method of production is essential to make the quality of product associated with our company," or "But we can't rely on the service of an outside supplier" rarely is an adequate answer to the question: "What is the economic advantage of maintaining or engaging in *this* manufacturing activity?" Enjoying the options of whether or not to engage in manufacturing and, if so, to what extent, the manufacturer should select the options that, on the basis of an objective quantitative analysis, offer a rewarding return on the shareholders' investment in the manufacturing activity.

Thus we have a three-dimensional definition of the manufacturing function:

· It is the physical function of generating products.
· It is the economic function of generating profits.
· It is the social function of generating change.

II

Questions

Why *and* how *are words so im-*
portant that they cannot be too
often used.
—Napoleon Bonaparte

It is not enough to be busy; so
are the ants. The question is:
What are we busy about?
—Henry David Thoreau

AMONG THE OLYMPIAN ATTRIBUTES and skills the industrial manager
is expected to display, the talent to ask the right question is paramount. It would be superfluous to cite examples of the countless
instances in which answers are accepted for the wrong or the super-
ficial question. Too often, regrettably, the wrong question is asked
or the right question is asked imprecisely. More often, no explicit
questions are asked, but impressively documented and elaborate
"answers" are proffered by operating management to fulfill vague
and contradictory corporate objectives.

What is the right question? *Why, what, when, where,* and *how*
frequently introduce the right question. It is easy for these questions
to be banal, but it is also possible for them to lead to more incisive
questions and to a recognition of the essential factors and assumptions surrounding the decisive question. Once the right question is
perceived and stated objectively, the "answers" are usually self-
evident and amenable to critical evaluation.

25

One of the most dramatic cases of posing the crucial questions of manufacturing strategy was demonstrated by the International Business Machines Corporation in developing and achieving full-scale production and installation of its System/360 data processing product family. Prior to 1960, IBM was primarily an assembler of computer components, while its strategic superiority lay in its marketing and business service capabilities. The decision to establish a major component manufacturing capability was actually made in 1960, a year and a half before the truly momentous decision in January 1962 to proceed with the development of a single compatible family of third-generation computers, subsequently identified as the System/360. The former strategy had been to design circuit components, to subcontract these component manufacturing requirements to external vendors, and then to assemble these components within IBM's own facilities. The initial rationale for expanding component manufacturing was to establish an assured source of supply satisfying production and delivery schedules most effectively; secondary considerations were to protect certain proprietary information concerned with circuitry production and to secure a manufacturing profit.

However, it was essential that the major advances in electronic technology be incorporated into the new family of computers. After a well-balanced evaluation, the alternative of monolithic integrated circuitry—a technology offering several theoretical advantages, which is actually used in RCA's Spectra 70 equipment and is still under active development by IBM and other computer manufacturers—was rejected in favor of hybrid integrated circuitry, designated "solid logic technology." This strategic decision was based upon the uncertainties surrounding the large-scale production of monolithic circuits and the inability to support the marketing schedule for the new computer family. This advanced electronic technology emphasized the importance of developing a comprehensive in-house component manufacturing capability. In 1962, design and erection of a $100 million semi-automated/batch manufacturing facility in East Fishkill, New York, were initiated.

Despite major commitments and farsighted planning, production difficulties were encountered when the new equipment was placed in production in 1964 and 1965; unanticipated metallurgical problems seriously curtailed IBM's own in-plant production of semiconductors for several months, while inadequate deliveries of other requirements from external vendors led to further delays. Both these serious deficiencies appear to underscore the soundness of IBM's manufacturing strategy, although the magnitude and many state-of-the-art characteristics of the System/360 programs amplified the inevitable start-up problems associated with launching an important new product group. The System/360 project witnessed the transformation of IBM from an assembler of components into a major manufacturing organization and the largest producer of integrated circuits in the world.

WHY?

"Why manufacture?" precedes all other questions. Until this question can be answered precisely, the objectives of the enterprise cannot be defined, and there are no useful standards available against which to measure the performance of either an ongoing or contemplated manufacturing activity.

"Why manufacture?" recognizes that the manufacturing function is usually optional. Although this attribute of being optional commonly is apparent for a new venture, it seldom receives more than a rhetorical tribute when an ongoing operation is under examination. In the latter case, attention may be focused upon peripheral questions rather than upon the axial question of why the organization is engaged in the specific manufacturing activity at all. Failure to cope with this central question leads to the perpetuation and often to the expansion of manufacturing activities that, while presumably meeting an important corporate objective when initially established, now no longer employ the resources of the organization as creatively as newly available alternative activities could.

The question "Why manufacture?" exhibits both aggressive and defensive facets. In general, the aggressive facets of the question seek an answer that offers a new source of profits within the immediate or foreseeable future; the defensive facets of the question seek an answer that protects or reduces the risk of possible erosion of a present source of profits. The answer to a specific *why* question may properly present both aggressive and defensive facets.

Of course, the simplest response to the *why* question is "To secure a manufacturing profit"—that is, to secure a profit contribution that would be lost to the enterprise if the specific manufacturing activity were to be discontinued. Classically, it is expected that the manufacturing profit will result in a rate of return on the total incremental investment in manufacturing at least commensurate with the return on other investment opportunities available to the enterprise. Measuring the manufacturing profit generally involves the use of rather rigorous managerial accounting techniques to define marginal costs —and, in many instances, marginal revenues—as well as the introduction of management judgment to establish an equitable schedule of transfer prices. Usually, the computational precision of a manufacturing profit can be questioned and subjected to more than one valid interpretation; contemporary accounting methods, however, enable the order of magnitude of the profit attributable to a particular manufacturing activity to be determined within fairly narrow limits. If the principal answer to the question "Why manufacture?" is "To secure a manufacturing profit," management must exercise constant vigilance to insure that this manufacturing profit is being generated and that it can be identified quantitatively. In its simplest form, the answer to this *why* question often involves the traditional "make or buy" analysis.

The other common aggressive facet to the question "Why manufacture?" is found in the response "To maintain, develop, or acquire some special technological capability." The present accelerating rate of technological advancement presents countless cases where this response is prudently farsighted. For example, many corporations engaged in serving or planning to serve the more sophisticated aerospace, nuclear, military equipment, computer, and research and development industries frequently must embark upon the development of a manufacturing capability simply to maintain a knowledge and facility of the technological progress in a selected field. In many instances, these decisions must be made with only the vaguest indications of the eventual profit contributions that may be derived from such a venture and with a historical awareness that an uncomfortably high percentage of such ventures are unsuccessful. Nevertheless, the alternative of avoiding such uncertain undertakings or of postponing a decision until the developmental crises have been overcome is often an unacceptable answer to the organization whose competitive strength lies in its technological leadership and competence.

The critical consideration when the response to the *why* question is "To maintain, develop, or acquire some special technological capability" is, again, *why*? Despite the difficulties in finding a valid quantitative answer, the ultimate answer to this question must still be "To secure a manufacturing profit" within the foreseeable future. An effort must be made to develop at least gross-order-of-magnitude limits of the potential market, the expected competitive structure of the industry, and the likely profit contribution of the venture. Such an undertaking should be re-evaluated frequently, initial forecasts should be continually refined as more reliable data becomes available, and the question "Why manufacture?" again should be posed to confirm or reject the initial answer.

From among many notable examples, perhaps one of the most easily recognized cases of differing strategic responses to this question "Why manufacture?" has been illustrated by the development and market distribution of commercial color television receiving sets. Virtually each of the conceivable responses to this question was adopted by at least one of the commercial electronic equipment manufacturers, and the prolonged period to achieve market acceptance of this new product has demonstrated vividly the vital role of a corporation's response to this particular strategic question. Organizations with some noteworthy technological competence or past success are especially prone to continuing, expanding, or adding to their manufacturing activities to nurture the egos and intellectual curiosity of management rather than to secure an identifiable manufacturing profit. Obviously, these responses—almost always unstated —will be discovered and excised from the enterprise when the right questions are asked imaginatively.

Among the defensive facets to the question "Why manufacture?" a common response is "To secure a reliable source of supply." Many times, an organization's competitive advantage is based upon having reliable internal sources of supply for components, subassemblies, or other manufacturing requirements. The magnitude of this advantage can be determined by exploring the sensitivity of operations to the hazards of drawing upon the alternative and supposedly unreliable external sources of supply.

However, in many other instances, the competitive importance of maintaining an extensive internal manufacturing capability is illusory—an excuse for "empire building" and for the perpetuation of marginal manufacturing activities that call for substantial resource investments yielding questionable tangible returns. There can be many excellent, even superior, ways of securing reliable sources of supply that avoid or minimize the requirements for an internal manufacturing capability. Among the more creative ways to secure external suppliers of adequate reliability are the programs of some of the larger retailing organizations—for example, Sears, Roebuck and Co.—to upgrade the operational and managerial proficiency of their suppliers. Comparable programs of the U.S. Department of Defense may also warrant emulation.

A similar response to the question "Why manufacture?" is "To assure product quality/reliability." The performance specifications of many products may permit few practicable alternatives to in-house manufacturing. When meeting rigid product specifications is essential, the evaluation of alternative external sources of supply seldom proceeds on a quantitative basis. Repeatedly, this question is answered subjectively; when in doubt, the so-called conservative error of selecting internal manufacturing in place of external supply seems to be preferred.

This may have been a prudent attitude in the past, but improved techniques of statistical analysis can now be employed routinely to ascertain the cost (or a range of costs) attributable to the possibility of external suppliers failing to meet product quality/reliability standards versus the cost of assuring fully that these standards would be met by establishing or maintaining an internal manufacturing capability. This question should be examined through the use of quantitative techniques of analysis before reaching an intuitive decision that external sources of supply are out of the question. Frequently, the illusion that other sources of supply cannot satisfy product quality/reliability standards provides an answer embraced in fear and ignorance—an unfounded justification for improvident internal manufacturing activities.

"The imperative need to respond rapidly to market changes or customer demands" is another answer to the question "Why manufacture?" Industries characterized by frequent and often unpredictable changes in product design (for example, those which deal in high-fashion apparel or whose activities are based upon advanced engineering technology) generally have manufacturing techniques and facilities that can shift swiftly to meet drastically revised product design criteria. It may be essential to maintain an integrated internal manufacturing capability to remain assured that the response to the market's tumultuous demands and opportunities will be timely and effective. In many cases, of course, an internal manufacturing capability may not be the best way to satisfy these requirements; it may be preferable to shift this burden to a larger or more specialized external supplier whose unique experience, larger operations, specialized equipment, or superior production control system offer swifter response characteristics than could be achieved internally. As always, rather than rely upon intuition or experience, the answer to this *why* question can and should be based upon an adequate quantitative evaluation of the profit potential and explicit risks of each reasonable internal and external source of supply.

Still another valid defensive response to the question "Why manufacture?" is "To protect proprietary information." This is a consideration of supreme importance in many operations—as in the manufacturing processes and product formulations for many companies in the chemical, pharmaceutical, and ethical drug industries. The violation of technological security can seriously undermine or even totally destroy the profitability of many operations. Thus, when the security of proprietary information is a foundation of an organization's competitive strength, the manufacturing function may be not merely optional but inevitable.

"The utilization of spare plant capacity" is a final example of a defensive response to the question "Why manufacture." Answers to this question usually lead to other questions:

- "Why is spare plant capacity available?"
- "Is this availability of excess plant capacity a near-term or a long-range situation?"
- "Is the need for this manufacturing capability likely to be temporary or is it a permanent requirement?"
- "What other uses for this existing plant capacity are presented by the organization's strategic manufacturing plans?"
- "How is the cost of this available plant capacity to be allocated to this manufacturing activity and to the company's other operations for purposes of justification, and for purposes of management accounting and profit control?"

The utilization of spare plant capacity can often be a shrewd way to develop a new or to expand an existing manufacturing activity with the possibility of attractive incremental earnings. On the other hand, marginal cost analyses often appear to justify the establishment of questionable manufacturing activities primarily because spare plant capacity happens to be available; strategically, the use of existing resources for an activity of dubious profitability may be myopic. Although the presence of unused plant capacity is an important consideration in the development of a manufacturing strategy, the most productive use for these capabilities can only be determined after the manufacturing strategy of the enterprise has been established and the other possible uses of these resources have been identified.

Thus the question "Why manufacture?" can be answered in many ways—aggressively as well as defensively. However, in a broad sense, the answer to this *why* question must be that the incremental income is an attractive return on the resources invested in the manufacturing activity compared with other investment opportunities that may be available—that is, to secure a manufacturing profit or to protect a profit position dependent upon manufacturing. This profit advantage derived through manufacturing may not be realized immediately, but the manufacturing strategy must state realistically the magnitude and timing of these incremental earnings in quantitative terms.

What?

Following the *why* question, we encounter the question "What to manufacture?" Although this question cannot be answered without a clear statement of the strategic reasons for and the objectives of a specific manufacturing activity, we face somewhat different options in determining *what* to manufacture. This question must be resolved by employing quantitative techniques to evaluate the anticipated profit characteristics of a manufacturing activity. It must also be resolved by employing techniques to evaluate anticipated managerial performance and competence.

Manufacturing strategy should impose gross limits on *what* to manufacture. Should an organization that manufactures electronic components and assembled products also manufacture its own chassis, caseworks, and cabinets or its own electrical components, such as drive motors, cable, and wiring devices? Very few electronic manufacturers attempt to produce these components; even if the profit contribution of these possible activities should be attractive, the diversion of management attention into unfamiliar technologies may be unwelcome. With few exceptions, management talent is a more precious resource than capital or physical facilities. An array of potentially profitable manufacturing activities may appear to be omnipresent, but the always limited time and skills of management are employed most rewardingly when focused upon a familiar and fairly narrow range of technologies. This attitude will often conflict —but is not irreconcilable—with a policy of corporate diversification. Whether intuitively or by conscious design, the manufacturing strategy of every enterprise places at least gross limits on *what* is to be manufactured. Although these limits generally exclude those technologies where management displays no special competence, the real answer to this *what* question must never be the timidity or complacency of management.

A manufacturing objective of The Gillette Company is to produce all components and assemblies critical to product performance and to subcontract all noncritical requirements. Thus all types of blades and razors are manufactured completely by the company within its own facilities; only steel strip and certain other basic raw materials meeting proprietary specifications are procured from an external source of supply. Similarly, all toiletries and the hair-care products of its subsidiary, The Toni Company, are compounded internally. While aerosol products were initially fabricated under contract by an external vendor, Gillette perceived this operation to be crucial to product performance. Superior competence has been acquired in this technology, and all major subsidiaries and divisions now fabricate their own aerosol products. However, with the exception of a critical plastic component in the Techmatic Razor and the plastic forming operations of the Paper Mate Division, all plastic requirements and all other packaging and promotional materials are procured from external sources. The technology associated with these materials and components is seldom complex, and numerous analyses have indicated that the corporation could secure attractive manufacturing profits by producing many of these products internally. Nevertheless, Gillette does not believe that the diffusion of managerial and technological talent required to engage in these non-critical manufacturing activities would be a prudent deployment of valued resources.

One facet of the question "What to manufacture?" is the extent of integration that promises to be most profitable. A common response to this *what* question is "Nothing!" However, when there are substantial reasons to manufacture, many subsequent questions must be explored to identify the manufacturing activities that appear to be either most profitable or, possibly, imperative.

- Should the enterprise engage in only assembling and finishing, or in the production of one or a few critical components, or in the production of components for others, or in the production of components and total assemblages?
- How far backward should the manufacturing function be integrated, and how many peripheral components, accessories, and subassemblies should be manufactured?
- How broadly should a manufacturer integrate across an industry?

In response to these questions, it is interesting to observe that the large airframe manufacturers seldom produce their own propulsion units; in the furniture industry, one manufacturer may specialize in the production of only Colonial wood chairs, another may produce chairs and case goods in designs of several periods, and still another may produce chairs, case goods, and upholstered goods in designs of many periods.

To say that the question "What to manufacture?" can be answered by projecting quantitatively the anticipated profit contribution of each option is often a misleading oversimplification. *What* to manufacture is both the taproot of manufacturing strategy and, generally, a major part of total corporate strategy. Although the answer to this question must be economically sound, its strategic implications often take it beyond the realm of the traditional make-or-buy analysis. The enterprise should manufacture what will maximize the return on the total resources available and what will strengthen its strategic effectiveness.

In addition to the extent of integration, another facet of the question "What to manufacture?" examines plant capacity in relation to expected market demand. Again, the possible responses to this question offer many options:

- Should a manufacturer of hydraulic pumps attempt to produce models in all sizes and characteristics or only those units that constitute the bulk of the market demand?
- If the latter option is selected, should the remainder of the market requirements be ignored (to be satisfied by manufacturing competitors), or should these units be manufactured to the pump manufacturer's specifications and under their label by external suppliers?
- When market demand is characterized by a wide variation in volume or product mix, should the manufacturing facilities be capable of meeting peak demand or only uniform base demand?
- If the former option is selected, can any use be made of excess plant capacity during the prolonged periods of substantial below-capacity operations?
- If the latter option is selected, can customer requirements during periods of peak demand be ignored, can the customers be re-educated, can external suppliers be drawn upon to satisfy customer needs, or can improved techniques of finished inventory control cope with the problem?

Answers to these questions affect both marketing and manufacturing strategies. Total corporate strategy frequently dictates that otherwise marginal manufacturing activities be undertaken to fulfill certain strategic objectives. Accepting these corporate objectives, senior management must always be apprised of the cost of undertaking these marginal manufacturing activities and more economical alternatives for meeting these product requirements must continually be investigated. Many of the factors influencing the response to this *what* question can be quantified, thereby leading to the development of a more effective marketing-manufacturing strategy.

Finally, in spite of the present limits that may have been placed upon the question "What to manufacture?" it remains questionable whether this function can ever be limited to present types of products or whether it should be expanded to encompass products that require new or different technologies.

- Can the manufacturer of machine tools survive without some internal electronic manufacturing capability?
- Must this capability be broadened to include digital computer and numerical control equipment?
- As computer directors and electronic control systems become

standard elements of machine tools and material handling equipment, can the manufacturers of this equipment continue to rely wholly upon external sources of supply for these major components and assemblies?

· Does management have any option other than to develop superior proficiency and facilities in these new technologies?

Often, a quantitative evaluation of this question may be negative and shortsighted; the real question is one of corporate existence and vitality. "What to manufacture?" rarely can be answered by "Only those products where our past experience gives us some special expertise" or by "Anything on which we can make a buck!" "What to manufacture?" is truly the most introspective question that can be asked by management; the answers to this question reveal the identity and the self-consciousness of an industrial corporation.

WHEN?

"When to manufacture?" is the next fundamental question to be resolved. Timing is inevitably an essential aspect of any strategic plan. History presents innumerable examples of the most carefully conceived and otherwise excellent plans that have failed for want of proper timing. Today's industrial environment of change accentuates the critical role of strategic timing; that is, the timely execution and, often, redirection of manufacturing activities.

The simplest and quite likely the most common response to the question "When to manufacture?" is "Throughout the entire life cycle of a product." When introducing a new model, the improvement of an established product, or even a new product well related to existing products, few manufacturers consider any other alternative than to undertake a certain mix of manufacturing activities as long as there is adequate market demand for the products. This response is common and often is valid in those industries where the life cycle of a product is not characterized by major technological development problems or by fundamental changes in product configuration or demand. The manufacturer of shoes, carpets, tires, or canned soup is included in this category; perhaps the distinguishing characteristic is that basically these products are commodities lacking any one-of-a-kind uniqueness or differentiation. However, once the initial response to the *when* question has resulted in a manufacturing activity, the question cannot be dismissed permanently; product and production technology as well as market expectations are always in a state of flux, and *now* may be *when* an existing manufacturing activity should be realigned or even discontinued. "When to manufacture?" is intertwined with the *why* and *what* questions, but its emphasis upon timing and its propensity to re-examine the latter questions give this question a special importance.

"When to manufacture?" leads numerous manufacturers to the strategically effective response "Only during the period of technological development and market introduction." An organization with a strong research and development capability whose products enjoy strong patent protection may find that large-scale manufacturing does not offer the most attractive return on the resources that would be required. It may elect to confine its manufacturing activities to those limited operations necessary to overcome all problems of commercial product development and to achieve market awareness and acceptance. Once these introductory goals have been secured, large-volume production and distribution may be achieved by arranging supply contracts with qualified external manufacturers; in certain cases—particularly when international sales are substantial—licensing other manufacturers to produce the product may be the most satisfactory way to meet burgeoning market demand and to realize an attractive, and comparatively risk-free, return.

A variation of this response is exemplified by the manufacturer whose primary sphere is the production of raw materials or components for sale to and fabrication by others, but who maintains a fully integrated albeit narrow manufacturing capability to stay in touch with market trends and the manufacturing problems of their industrial consumers. Although the major producers of basic chemicals are not engaged in the fabrication of consumer plastics, several of the major chemical companies maintain small plastic fabricating operations to improve their understanding of the consumer plastic market and of the needs of their customers—the plastic extruding, molding, and fabricating companies. Thus the response to the question "When to manufacture?" may specify a schedule of very different types of manufacturing activities at different periods throughout the life cycle of a product.

"When to manufacture?" leads many manufacturers to the opposite response—"Only after the market has been established or stabilized." An organization whose primary competitive strength is the efficiency of its manufacturing operations or the breadth of its distribution structure—but whose research and development skills or financial resources may be limited—may find that its most effective strategic response is to postpone market entry until after the problems associated with technological development have been overcome and market demand can be determined with considerable assurance. This response avoids the risk and the often prodigious commitments of capital, management, and personnel with special skills which are encountered in undertaking a product development program that could result in only limited success or even failure. Naturally, this response also embodies the risk that the carefully planned and successful product development efforts of competitors may preclude the opportunity for market entry at any time in the future on an attractive basis. "When to manufacture?" is the question that introduces the critical dimension of time into manufacturing strategy. In many cases, the so-called right answer to this question can prove to be the dominant feature in the successful execution of total corporate strategy.

WHERE?

The next question, "Where to manufacture?" is of obvious strategic importance. Strategy is always dependent upon recognizing the consequences and exploiting the opportunities of geography, or terrain. As is true for each of the preceding questions, once answered satisfactorily, this question must be re-examined periodically to evaluate the impact of the product's life cycle, and of changes both inside and outside the organization, upon *where* the manufacturing activity can be undertaken most effectively.

The geographic location or locations at which specific manufacturing operations are to be performed is the first consideration in answering this question. Although the quantitative techniques of plant location studies can be a useful approach to this problem, these efforts frequently are of limited value when the strategic objectives of the enterprise are not clearly defined and understood; the growing importance of international markets introduces unique influences into this problem.

- What are the geographic and technological trends of the markets to be served?
- What are the expected developments of production technology (for example, modular fabrication of major components and subassemblies)?
- What are the implications of forecast developments in transport and in physical distribution?
- What are the ways in which one facility is to reinforce or cover other facilities in the event of disruption of operations?
- What strategic realignments are planned for manufacturing mix and capabilities?

These illustrative queries suggest the questions that influence manufacturing strategy of the enterprise. Unfortunately, too many plant location studies are based upon doing present jobs in more or less the same way they are being done today and upon present sales volumes being extrapolated at some empirical growth rate for an arbitrary number of the years into the future. This approach in no way capitalizes on the advantages to be gained through pursuing imaginative strategies of production technology development, inventory management, physical distribution, and market development. Today, "Where to manufacture?" can only be answered profitably by relating the question to a comprehensive—often a global—strategy of manufacturing.

Another facet of the question "Where to manufacture?" is whether the locations are to be temporary or permanent. In a highly fluid situation, it may be judicious to select on a temporary basis one or more points at which to manufacture certain products within the immediate future, recognizing that more propitious permanent locations will be selected as soon as either the technology or market demand or competitive structure of the industry has clarified or stabilized. This stance usually expresses an implicit manufacturing, and corporate, strategy of "wait and see" and is encountered frequently in industries that exhibit volatile characteristics of technology or market demand: for example, the more advanced state-of-the-art industries, such as those associated with space exploration or, more traditionally, the industries associated with high-fashion apparel. Although temporary locations usually place a premium on mobility and flexibility, these advantages are frequently acquired at the price of less-than-optimum owning and operating costs; facilities and plant layout often are not the most efficient, the levels of mechanization may be somewhat lower than otherwise desired, and transportation patterns and distribution costs may be compromised.

In numerous situations, a superior strategy is one of alert quiescence; it may be implemented most economically by establishing certain manufacturing activities at temporary locations. However, this response should not be an excuse for indecisiveness or a lack of strategy; once an opportunity presents itself for enacting an aggressive manufacturing strategy, this can usually be launched most powerfully from permanent manufacturing bases. Permanence, of course, varies greatly from industry to industry; a permanent location for a steel rolling mill should be satisfactory for about 40 years, whereas a permanent location for an electronics operation may have an expected life of 36 months.

One other facet of "Where to manufacture?" is whether the locations are to be in existing or in new facilities. After determining geographic locations and temporary versus permanent locations, the question of existing versus new facilities can be largely resolved by quantitative analyses of the available alternatives. These analyses not only can evaluate the physical characteristics of each alternative but also can measure the economy of various combinations of financing each alternative (including direct ownership, rental, and leaseback). Emotional factors should not lead to a decision to erect new facilities when the imaginative rejuvenation and utilization of existing facilities could satisfy all strategic objectives more economically; on the other hand, continuing operations in uneconomical older facilities cannot be condoned.

When the decision is made to erect new facilities or to reconstruct existing facilities extensively, the design of these works should emphasize flexibility and resiliency to accommodate future changes. If the answers to the several questions "Where to manufacture?" have been based upon a carefully constructed strategy of manufacturing, a modest increase in initial investment due to these enhanced design criteria will be amply recovered through the facilities' abilities to accept most of the unforeseen demands of the future economically and with minimum disruption to ongoing operations.

"Where to manufacture?" confronts the elemental strategic considerations of logistics and geographic opportunity. The answers to these *where* questions may not be fixed in terms of 50 or, in many cases, even 10 years, yet they must be sufficiently well founded and clearly defined to justify major investments in plant and manufacturing facilities being undertaken aggressively and with conviction. Despite some unavoidable characteristics of permanence, the answers to these *where* questions must also display sufficient flexibility (in some cases, perhaps even mobility) to cope with unanticipated strategic responses in the future. And, most importantly, the answers to these *where* questions must array the manufacturing capabilities of the enterprise in a way that will maximize the effectiveness of manufacturing, marketing, and financial resources.

How?

The final fundamental question "How to manufacture?" tends to focus more upon engineering and operational factors than the previous questions. This question is considered last because it can seldom be answered intelligently until the previous questions have received at least tentative responses. Often, preoccupation with the mechanics of *how* to manufacture masks the logical precedence of the other fundamental questions. Of course, *how* to manufacture may have to be investigated rather extensively before conclusive answers to these other questions can be accepted.

One of the first implications of the question "How to manufacture?" is the scale of operations. In many industries, the scale of operations can be expanded from a comparatively low-volume plant by the expedient of linear addition—adding more of the same type of equipment with little change in the unit costs of production. As an example, the installation of additional looms permits the hourly output of a textile mill to be expanded in very small increments without any appreciable effect on unit product costs; this is one of the principal reasons why the textile industry is not characterized by very large manufacturing complexes. However, it is quite common for the scale of operations to define the technology of the manufacturing process. For example, up to a certain volume level, a food-processing operation cannot justify the installation of bulk receiving, storage, distribution, and automatic metering systems for ingredients such as sugar (liquid or granulated), milk, flour, and shortenings; but once this critical volume level is passed, the technology of manufacturing changes radically and the unit costs of production are reduced perceptibly.

The scale of operations cannot be determined solely on the basis of engineering economy studies but must be established in response to clearly defined objectives of manufacturing strategy. A strategy of manufacturing must be founded upon a full understanding of the several scales of operation that may be feasible and of the operational advantages and constraints associated with each of these options. Because the production technologies of each of these scales of operation often are quite different and may be relatively new and unproven, "How to manufacture?" is truly a question of manufacturing strategy rather than a question of engineering design and operating know-how. Engineering enthusiasm has been known to create outstanding operations that failed because the scale of operations was not matched realistically to the manufacturing proficiency or to the marketing objectives of the enterprise. On the other hand, reluctance to define an imaginative manufacturing strategy has led to the installation of operations at a scale that soon proved to be inadequate and prematurely obsolete.

Another facet of the question "How to manufacture?" seeks to establish the most appropriate type of production equipment and facilities. Today, this aspect of the question must determine the technological sophistication and the degree of automation that are required to fulfill the strategic objectives of the enterprise most effectively. Although extraordinary achievements in automation are being witnessed almost every day, many of those which receive the most notoriety in the trade press fail abjectly when measured against the standard of profit contribution. The selection and design of production equipment and facilities require a kind of clairvoyance to predict future product configurations, market characteristics, and— perhaps most interestingly—the type and rate of technological change that are likely to occur. Whenever a primary management criterion of design is simply that a facility is to be "the most automated plant . . . ," it is usually observed that this untidy statement reveals an absence of manufacturing strategy formulation. Automation, in itself, is rarely a virtue, nor is it necessarily a profit-producing attribute; however, when employed with purpose and precision, it can be a potent weapon in the armory of the manufacturing strategist.

The steel industry presents one of the most dramatic illustrations of the relevance of each of these questions, especially of the important question, "How to manufacture?" Within recent decades, this industry developed a number of notable improvements in the area of innovative mechanization and automation—continuous wide strip mills, continuous pickling lines, continuous galvanizing lines, electrolytic tin plate process, electronic inspection of tin plate, stretch process for reducing tubes, electrically welded pipe, multiple block wire drawing, ultrasonic testing, mechanical scarfing, and high-top-pressure blast furnaces. With the introduction of several major advances in steelmaking technology in the early 1950's, however, the industry changed almost the entire process of manufacturing steel. By the mid-1960's, the industry installed advanced facilities at an increasing rate. During 1966, capital expenditures were $2.0 billion—more than twice the annual rate during the 1961–1963 period.

The basic oxygen process, vacuum degassing, continuous casting, and computer control are among the principal technologies exerting a significant impact on steelmaking. The basic oxygen process (BOP) was the first such manufacturing advance to be commercially developed. In 1952, the first commercial installation of basic oxygen furnaces of 36-ton capacity began operation at the Linz plant of the United Austrian Iron and Steel Works Company. The first oxygen furnace in the United States was installed in 1954 by the McLouth Steel Corporation, a comparatively small steel producer. Among the eight major producers, the first oxygen furnace was installed in 1957 by the Jones & Laughlin Steel Corporation. Although 50 furnaces had been installed by the late 1950's, technological problems limited the design capacity of these units to not more than 80 tons. Beginning in 1958, meanwhile, a declining demand for steel curtailed the industry's capital expenditure programs for several years. Engineering advances in the early 1960's yielded operating economies that justified the installation of large units of 200- to 300-ton capacity and had overcome product and air-pollution limitations inherent in the earlier versions of BOP facilities. By 1962, other major steel producers began installing large-scale BOP units. Among the three largest producers, United States Steel Corporation and Bethlehem Steel Corporation installed their first oxygen units in 1963 and 1964, respectively, and Republic Steel Corporation installed its first oxygen furnace in 1965. However, the open-hearth process is being replaced at an accelerating rate by the basic oxygen furnace; the oxygen furnace produced 2.5 percent of United States steel output in 1956, 12 percent in 1964, and 25 percent in 1966. At the close of 1966, the annual BOP steelmaking capacity of the United States was approximately 38 million tons and expansion to 72 million tons by 1970 was forecast. Since 1962, BOP steel production in the United States has represented a much larger proportion of total production than it has abroad; while open-hearth production has *decreased* by 15 percent in the United States since 1952, such production has *increased* by 113 percent in the rest of the world. This improved steelmaking process is credited with reducing the production cost of steel by an estimated $5 per ton—approximately 40 percent lower than those applicable to the high-cost, obsolete open-hearth furnaces they replaced. This differential, however, is much smaller when compared with the industry's newer, modernized open hearths equipped with oxygen lances.

The basic oxygen process has now become a widely accepted technology within the industry. But spray steelmaking, a process developed in the Sheffield laboratories of the British Iron and Steel Research Association, could portend another significant technological advance in manufacturing. This spray process is a batch process (capable of continuous operations); its refining action is virtually instantaneous; it may be able to accept as much as 40 percent scrap; and it is purported to offer several operating advantages. In 1966, the Millom Hematite Ore & Iron Company in Millom, Cumberland, England, placed in operation a prototype plant producing 10-ton batches of steel. Using the spray process, this organization is scheduled to reach a steel output of 3,000 tons per week by 1968 and 9,000 tons per week by the early 1970's.

Continuous casting is the technological challenge confronting the industry in the mid-1960's. Full-scale continuous casting facilities were placed on stream by U. S. Steel in Gary, Indiana, and by National Steel Corporation in Weirton, West Virginia, in 1967. Nevertheless, the new process is still fraught with engineering difficulties that have not been fully resolved, with two competing equipment configurations—the vertical or "straight mold" unit and the "low head" or "curved mold" unit—and with uncertainty in the minds of conservative operators concerning its ability to produce rimmed steel meeting the quality standards for automotive and appliance sheet and tinplate. The conviction that these development difficulties can be overcome, however, coupled with possible economies associated with continuous casting—yield increases of about 10 percent and capital costs approximately half those required for comparable conventional primary rolling and ingot facilities—may indicate that this new technology will become the standard of the industry within the near future. Currently, a most significant development is connected with *continuous* continuous casting; a prototype plant is being erected by the Koppers Company, Inc., in Aviles, Spain, while Concast, Inc. (an affiliate of Concast A.G., of Zurich, Switzerland) is erecting a facility for the Algoma Steel Corporation, Ltd., in Canada that is capable of forming semifinished steel shapes.

The steel industry—in concert with almost all manfacturing industries—is continually extending the application of computers for process direction and control. Computer directors are becoming an integral part of both hot strip and cold mills; they are invaluable in establishing metallurgical and timing factors for basic oxygen furnaces and constitute an essential component of continuous casting plants. Computer capabilities make it technologically feasible to realize the industry's goal of transforming steelmaking from a batch operation into a continuous process. The significance of all these advances in technology is emphasized by noting that the industry's capital expenditures program for the second half of the decade is almost double the capital expenditures program recorded during the first half.

Thus "How to manufacture?" is not a question that can be delegated entirely to engineering or operating management, nor is it a question that can be answered most effectively without the frame of reference of the strategic manufacturing objectives of the organization. Response to this question must answer *how* the contemplated method of manufacturing will fulfill the strategic objectives of the enterprise better than any feasible alternative methods. Today's advanced production systems and complex manufacturing technologies demand that strategy formulation be cognizant of and understand all of the available options of *how* the manufacturing activity can be performed.

This discussion of some of the questions that must be posed continually about both ongoing and contemplated manufacturing activities in no sense is meant to be exhaustive. It has only sought to illustrate the types of questions that must be resolved objectively and with conviction whenever any manufacturing activity is under scrutiny. Although the importance of searching for the "right" questions is emphasized, it is apparent that useful answers to these questions cannot be developed without a clear definition and an understanding of the manufacturing strategy of the enterprise. Superior responses to *why, what, when, where,* and *how* to manufacture must meet wholly and creatively the organization's manufacturing objectives. Therefore, our attention will next focus upon the processes by which these manufacturing objectives are to be established.

III

Objectives

Everything that looks to the future elevates human nature; for never is life so low or so little as when occupied with the present.
—Walter Savage Landor

Never look down to test the ground before taking your next step; only he who keeps his eye fixed on the far horizon will find his right road.
—Dag Hammarskjöld

IN EVERY WALK of life, the extraordinary practitioner is the one who has perceived some worthwhile objective—usually near the commencement of his career—has defined it precisely, then has pursued this objective with single-minded resolution. The composer or conductor of great music, the compassionate medical diagnostician or surgeon, the dedicated public administrator or statesman, and the selfless teacher or educational leader have all achieved eminence because of their ability to perceive—somewhat differently from their contemporaries—an objective that they have proceeded to pursue with tenacious devotion. Of course an objective, to be meaningful, cannot be so distant that it is not humanly attainable. However, superiority is earned only by men or organizations that establish an objective beyond the routine and that set out with diligence and determination to reach this objective.

47

Although single-mindedness is not an uncommon personal attribute, it is never one easily instilled in an industrial organization. An organization is composed of many persons, who are both individuals and members of various subgroups; each of these persons and groups may have interests and objectives that are in conflict with those of the organization as a whole. Divergent objectives can be expected of the many groups concerned with and affected by the activities of an industrial enterprise: the employees (and their unions), the managers, the shareholders, the customers, the government authorities, and the total community. Amid this welter of differing aims and purposes, the industrial manager is charged with establishing organizational objectives that both assure the healthy advancement of the organization and enlist the enthusiasm and support of the many interested parties both inside and outside the organization.

Establishing the manufacturing objectives of an enterprise first requires the adoption of an organizational point of view that, if possible, will be reasonably congruent with the various points of view expressed by the many parties associated with the organization. Although the viewpoints of each of these parties have some legitimacy, that of the shareholders generally is the one which polarizes the other interests most satisfactorily. The shareholders are the only party whose interest in the enterprise may be considered to be total; the enterprise—and, consequently, the shareholders—can prosper only if the interests of the other parties can be resolved and satisfied.

It has been noted that the economic function of manufacturing is the generation of profits and that this can also be stated as providing a rewarding return on the shareholders' investment in the manufacturing activity. To present a general definition, the principal objective of any manufacturing activity is to maximize the market value of the shareholders' equity in the enterprise. Regardless of how well other goals may appear to be met, if the market value of the shareholders' equity is not growing at a rate equal to or faster than that of other industrial corporations, new shareholders and equity funds cannot be attracted to the enterprise; present shareholders may become discouraged and defensive and possibly may seek to curtail or even to discontinue its operations. Thus an industrial corporation failing to enhance the market value of the shareholders' equity inevitably fails to satisfy the legitimate interests of the employees, the managers, the customers, the government, and the total community. Although these interests present certain checks and constraints, their aims and purposes can be fulfilled only within the context of a viable enterprise that meets in a superior way the economic objectives of the shareholders.

To maximize the market value of the shareholders' equity—although a laudable goal—is rarely an immediately useful way of defining the objectives of manufacturing. At least three often-conflicting dimensions of this definition present difficulties in translating the general objective into specific goals and meaningful standards of performance.

First, every person or organization is properly preoccupied with the need to define and attain certain near-term objectives. Second, it is essential that the long-range objectives of the enterprise be defined and, when appropriate, that efficacious action be initiated to secure these objectives; often the long-range objectives do not coincide with more immediate goals, and efforts taken to attain them detract from the ability to fulfill satisfactorily the near-term objectives. And finally—because the future cannot be foreseen with certainty—the third primary objective of manufacturing strategy must be flexibility. Again, this objective seldom coincides with either the specific immediate or long-range objectives, and it can only be satisfied by diluting to some extent the impact of our efforts to maximize these other objectives. Therefore, a coherent and well-focused strategy of manufacturing must be formulated from an effective combination or mix of these three dimensions of our general definition of manufacturing objectives.

NEAR-TERM OBJECTIVES

An amplified investigation of the first dimension of manufacturing strategy—the definition and attainment of certain near-term objectives—reveals the daily conflicts encountered by operating management. Invariably, the near-term objective receiving greatest attention is the profit contribution attributable to a specific manufacturing activity. However, it is a bland simplification to define this objective as "the maximization of current profits," for such an objective is seldom compatible with either the other near-term objectives or the long-range and flexibility objectives of the enterprise. Thus immediate profit objectives must be tempered by other objectives.

Present-day concepts of managerial accounting accept the techniques of profit planning—a management process to select, evaluate, budget, monitor, and control the allocation of resources to any contemplated or ongoing industrial operation. The profit plan not only establishes near-term profit objectives but also must introduce and resolve the resource requirements and economic implications of fulfilling all other strategic objectives during an operating period—perhaps six months or one year—within the immediate future. For example, a strategic objective of manufacturing may be to establish several diverse production activities in a new, highly mechanized, consolidated facility with expanded capacity. Given the attractive long-range returns or enhanced flexibility anticipated for this new facility, the profit plans for operating periods within the immediate future will reflect the unfavorable influence—owing to relocation, start-up, and learning costs—upon near-term profit objectives of the simultaneous pursuit of the longer-range objectives. Profit planning offers an excellent way for management to explore the implications and relationships of objectives, to select the most fertile mix of objectives and—in implementing the profit plan—to initiate the first phase of a strategic plan of manufacturing.

Profit planning should be focused continually upon maximizing the return on the shareholders' investment rather than solely upon maximizing gross or net profits on sales, near-term profits, or even total profits. Frequently, the simple enlargement of profits does not call for exceptional management ability; profits are often "bought" by less perspicacious managers who are indiscriminately pursuing the siren call of growth. Avoiding the temptation of generalizations, it can still be noted that numerous manufacturing activities are undertaken because of their incremental and supposedly riskless contribution to profits; in many cases, this profit contribution may represent a questionable return on the required resource investments, and more attractive returns may be offered by alternative (perhaps nonmanufacturing) investment opportunities. Thus profit planning should be directed toward fulfilling the foremost near-term objective—maximizing the return on the shareholders' investments in manufacturing activities—in ways that promise at least to equal or exceed the anticipated profitability of other investment opportunities.

Return on investment is counterpoised by the other near-term objective: managerial control. Managerial control is exerted to acquire mastery over both the internal behavior and the external environment of the enterprise sufficient to plan and predict its performance with a fairly high degree of certainty. Managerial control is present when management truly *runs* the enterprise, when adequate constraints are imposed upon the more variable factors influencing the enterprise, and when untoward events can be identified promptly and overcome effectively. Communication and discipline are the two principal aspects of managerial control.

Management cannot exercise control over an operation if it does not possess a rapid and responsive multiplex system of communications. Although this discussion need not digress into the complex field of the design of management information systems, a near-term as well as long-range objective of manufacturing strategy must be the development and maintenance of adequate systems of communication. It may not be necessary for the strategy of manufacturing to specify the mechanics of these communications systems, but it must specify realistically the required performance of these communications systems. Manufacturing strategy may often suggest the near-term objective of establishing a type of communications system radically different from that required for present operations; the immediate development of this new system will assure its being fully operational in time to support the subsequent development of the organization's manufacturing strategy.

Similarly, management cannot exercise control over an operation if it is not subject and responsive to the discipline of management. A common area of lack of control due to a lack of discipline—or sometimes a lack of communications—is union-management relations. A near-term objective of manufacturing strategy must always be to achieve or maintain honorable contractual and working relationships with labor unions or other employee representatives—recognizing fairly the contributions and just interests of the unions, but refusing to allow the prerogatives and consequent responsibilities of management to be eroded. In many cases where union-management relations have deteriorated badly or where present relations can no longer be tolerated by management, manufacturing strategy may dictate that the paramount near-term objective be to realign these unacceptable union-management relations, even if this requires the serious loss of current earnings. Absence of discipline and adequate management control indicates an organization in the process of dissolution.

Discipline can also be a near-term objective in other areas of manufacturing. Enhanced management control may be needed in the realms of product design, manufacturing engineering, and production scheduling and control; deficiencies in these areas are often attributed to poor communications, when a lack of discipline may be the correct explanation. Manufacturing strategies have been jeopardized by insufficient discipline being exercised over the methods of financing manufacturing facilities. Management control may also have to exert greater influence over the sources of supply for raw materials, components, or subassemblies as well as over the methods and channels of distribution. Although management can become obsessed with the presumed need to exercise absolute control over all aspects of both the internal behavior and the external environment of an enterprise, it must develop an organization sufficiently well disciplined to implement a manufacturing strategy by conscious action rather than by hope and good luck; any lesser standard of discipline is a violation of the authority and responsibilities entrusted to management.

Thus the near-term objectives of manufacturing strategy may be summarized as:

- The maximization of the shareholders' return on the investments in manufacturing activities.
- The development and maintenance of adequate management control over the manufacturing activities of the enterprise.

All other near-term objectives of consequence ultimately fuse into one of these two objectives.

LONG-RANGE OBJECTIVES

Near-term objectives offer excellent standards against which to measure current performance, but they seldom impart a sense of strategic direction to the manufacturing activities of an enterprise. Although the conformance of current operations to long-range ob-

jectives cannot be measured with the same directness as conformance to near-term objectives, useful long-range objectives can be
selected and the conformance of current operations to these objectives can be measured indirectly. Long-range objectives are to be
selected that expand the organization's profitable mastery over both
its external environment and its internal behavior; conformance to
these objectives can be evaluated by employing useful and progressive measures of competitive strength (external) and efficiency
(internal).

The two most common measures of competitive strength are
growth and *stability;* both these measures evaluate the vitality of
the manfacturing and the marketing activities of an enterprise.
Long-range growth objectives can be stated in several valid ways.
The rate of sales growth is usually the first method of measuring
corporate growth. Alone, an attractive rate of sales growth is no
assurance of prosperity or even of corporate survival; as part of a
strategic pattern, however, the rate of sales growth in carefully defined areas may be a useful standard against which to measure the
conformance of current operations to long-range objectives. The
rate of earnings growth is often the next method of measuring the
growth of an organization; this measure can evaluate indirectly the
shareholders' long-range rate of return on their investment in manufacturing activities.

Among other long-range growth objectives, the expansion of
selected product lines, the increase in market share in specific
market segments, and the enlargement of the scope of market being
served by the enterprise are goals offering standards against which
current operations can be measured in useful ways. To some extent,
manufacturing strategy must always be directed toward the fulfillment of one or more of these long-range growth objectives—often
at the cost of being unable to satisfy optimally the near-term objective of profit maximization. In establishing these long-range growth
objectives, it is essential to define them precisely and to select them
on the basis of their quantitative long-range expectation of enhancing the shareholders' return on their investment; the pursuit of
growth solely for the prestige of bigness often is the pursuit of a
will-o'-the-wisp, leading to a distended, ungainly, and unprofitable
economic organism.

Along with growth, stability is the other measure of the competitive strength of an industrial organization. Although this objective seeks to minimize the seasonal and cyclical fluctuations in sales volume, its most important function is to overcome fluctuations in sales volume, earnings, and return on assets due to supposedly random influences—actions of competitors and inconsistent internal performance. The identification and elimination of the factors that cause fluctuations in sales volume and the establishment of the conditions necessary to assure sound growth of sales volume constitute a long-range stability objective of manufacturing strategy. Another long-range stability objective should be to minimize fluctuations in earnings. This objective frequently is associated with the achievement of still another long-range stability objective—the uniform utilization of full plant capacity. While it is true that stability seldom can be sustained over any prolonged period, a long-range objective of manufacturing invariably is to secure in one or more critical operating areas a higher degree of stability than that possessed by one's competitors. Stability usually means greater resilience with which to withstand unexpected reverses as well as greater freedom of maneuver with which to exploit unexpected opportunities. In each industrial situation, manufacturing strategy must recognize the prerequisites for stability and must determine the steps required to fulfill these prerequisites if adequate mastery over the enterprise's external environment is to be secured.

Standards against which to measure conformity of current operations to the other primary long-range objective—mastery over internal behavior—usually introduce various measures of efficiency. The engineer defines efficiency as the ratio of the output of a physical system to its input; correspondingly, the economist defines efficiency as the ratio of the output of an economic system to its input. The efficiency of a physical system may approach but never exceed 100 percent, whereas the efficiency of an economic system should always exceed 100 percent. Because the margin by which this efficiency exceeds 100 percent is defined as profit, profit is the measure of economic efficiency. Thus economic efficiency is another way of measuring our primary objective—the maximization of the shareholders' return on their investment in manufacturing activities.

The long-range rate of return of current operations is seldom realistically measurable, however, so efficiency must be measured by other standards. One of the more common long-range objectives is the maintenance of high turnover rates. Return on sales is the most general turnover rate—an obvious but not always meaningful index of performance. Other indexes of performance—such as turnover of net worth, turnover of working capital, and turnover of inventory—may be more useful objectives and measures of operating efficiency.

When focused upon the salient measures of performance, the analysis of both operating and financial ratios may suggest long-range as well as near-term objectives and standards by which to evaluate the efficiency of manufacturing activities. As previously noted when discussing growth, turnover must be not merely a measure of velocity or busyness but an interim measure of profitability. Although the pertinent turnover ratios may differ from one organization to another, certain meaningful turnover ratios can provide an incisive measure of both the efficiency with which certain critical resources are being employed and the conformance of current operations to long-range strategic objectives.

Another useful measure of efficiency—that is, the enterprise's mastery over its internal behavior—is the depth of manufacturing skills. The depth and capability of management are always paramount but are most difficult to measure. Although past achievements cannot be ignored, the better measures of management strength may be the recent and potential professional growth of each manager, the varied job experiences to which each manager is being exposed, the formal managerial skills being mastered by each manager, and, inevitably, the sheer number of competent managers. Several types of so-called management audits can provide progressive albeit crude measures of management strength.

Today, the depth of skills in manufacturing research and product development may rival management's talents in importance. Although strategic objectives usually cannot be stated in terms of specific outputs of production or product technology, coincident objectives can be established and defined in terms of the anticipated research and development capabilities that will be needed to fulfill these long-range technological objectives; a strategic plan can then specify interim research and development goals, thereby offering standards against which current operations can be assessed.

Finally, the conscious upgrading of both the types and numbers of skilled technicians in the labor force can be a major strategic objective of manufacturing. This type of training and personal improvement program should be directed toward meeting specific technological objectives of the enterprise rather than the educational whims or desires of individuals. On the other hand, the rapid pace of technological evolution coupled with the uncertainty of the exact job requirements of the future suggest that management should be somewhat prodigal in the technical education and upgrading of the labor force to assure an adequate source of the right categories of skilled technicians when needed. The long-range objective of enlarging and strengthening manufacturing skills, therefore, can pervade all levels of an industrial organization.

One final measure of efficiency can be the age of physical assets. Although balance-sheet analyses indicate approximate chronological age, the more useful—and difficult—measure of age is technological age. The technological age of most physical assets, such as plant and machinery, can be determined only by objective and frequent engineering appraisals that recognize both the obsolescence and physical deterioration of these facilities. Although a few cases can be cited where comparatively old facilities are almost "as good as new," the pattern in most manufacturing industries is that technological age is appreciably greater than revealed by chronological indexes. Many cases can be cited where, because of a lack of strategic planning or imaginative engineering, facilities are technologically obsolete a few years or even months after being placed on stream. A revealing measure of the age of physical assets is the ratio of current capital expenditures for new plant and machinery versus current depreciation expenses. The contemporary experience of a continued inflationary bias in the economy plus rapid technological development commends establishing the long-range objective that this ratio be significantly more than unity. The strategic objectives of manufacturing should also monitor the age of one other class of physical assets—inventories. Each of these standards for gauging the technological age of physical assets can be an effective method of measuring the conformance of current operations to the long-range manufacturing objectives of the enterprise.

Although manufacturing strategy may popularly suggest exploiting growth opportunities through both internal development and external acquisition, corporate stability often is a prior and more rewarding strategic objective. Stability is commonly referred to as consolidation, cost cutting, or modernization. These goals are always a responsibility of operational management; organizational stability, on the other hand, frequently can become a primary objective of manufacturing strategy. To achieve this objective, it usually is necessary to enact a strategic program to which a major portion of the enterprise's resources must be committed and which may have to be scheduled over a period of several years.

Stability is a primary objective of Armco Steel Corporation's Project 600. This five-year plant improvement and cost reduction program, budgeted at $600 million, is directed toward strengthening the corporation's manufacturing capabilities and competitive stance.

Similarly, during the tumultuous and disappointing years following its unpropitious merger, the Olin Mathieson Chemical Corporation embarked upon a carefully planned and controlled operations, facilities, and profit improvement program in 1960. It subsequently scheduled a program from 1963 to 1968 focused upon transforming each of its divergent industrial activities into an enterprise generating a return on assets at least comparable to the upper third of its competition. The capital expenditures to implement this strategy have amounted to $100 million in a single year, and the accomplishments have ranged from construction of the world's largest phosphoric acid and ammonia plants to tangible reductions of $288,500 in outbound freight costs for its Forest Products Division during 1965 and 1966.

Even though the strategy for the subsequent five-year period may give priority to growth objectives, this intensive pursuit of corporate stability has resulted in enhanced competitive effectiveness plus satisfactory and continuing profit improvement. Stability is always a strategic objective of primary importance; its priority vis-à-vis corporate growth is determined more by whether existing manufacturing operations exhibit an acceptable degree of stability than by the inevitable presence of growth opportunities.

FLEXIBILITY

In concert with both near-term and long-range objectives, the third primary objective of manufacturing strategy is flexibility; that is, the recognition of partial ignorance. If the future could be foreseen with certainty, flexibility would be a meaningless and even an enervating objective. However, since our most careful forecasts and expectations of the future can never project the future exactly as it will be realized, all workable plans must exhibit sufficient flexibility to accommodate unforeseeable contingencies without endangering or aborting the total plan. Each objective of flexibility is an acknowledgment either that our near-term or long-range objectives may prove to have been defined incorrectly or may prove more elusive—if not impossible—to attain than anticipated; or, most commonly, that the future can be expected to deviate from forecasts in unpredictable and uncontrollable ways. In almost every instance, the satisfaction of flexibility objectives necessitates compromising one or more of the other strategic objectives of manufacturing.

The judicious introduction of flexibility is one of the critical factors that transforms an otherwise long-range plan into a strategic plan. This objective accepts both the unattainability and the undesirability of unlimited flexibility, but it perceives and circumvents the circumstances in which excessive rigidity could invite disaster. Flexibility objectives offer alternative courses and resources with which to avoid or weather the strategist's Scylla and Charybdis— the twin terrors created by the contingencies of environmental change and of competitive response. Similarly, to the mariners of ancient times, the horrors of rocky Scylla and swirling Charybdis resided not only in their annihilating proclivities but also in the uncertainty of their exact location and time of occurrence. Rather than pursuing near-term and long-range objectives frontally and with apparent maximum efficiency, flexibility objectives often result in a strategy in which the safeguarding of present positions and the consolidation of subsequent gains assume major importance. Flexibility objectives seek to temper the dramatic, exposed, and potentially vulnerable plan; to impart defensive features to an exuberantly aggressive plan; and to establish a strategy of manufacturing that can absorb reverses and exploit alternative opportunities.

The objective of flexibility exhibits both an external countenance —seeking to minimize the impact of contingencies upon the enterprise—and an internal countenance—seeking to strengthen the response of the enterprise to contingencies. Further, the external features of this objective may be categorized either as aggressive or defensive.

The number of prolific technologies in which an organization displays a recognized competence is one measure of aggressive external flexibility. The increasing rate of technological change and the observed half-life phenomenon of product profitability and market acceptability are warnings that—in today's environment of scientific and engineering ferment—the specialist in one or even a few limited technologies may face obsolescence and possible extinction overnight. The aggressive exploration and development of new technological fields can be a pre-emptive assault upon this contingency. The vitality of manufacturing research and product development is another measure of the objective of aggressive external flexibility; thoughtfully directed and controlled, these activities offer the only certain way to product/service superiority and market leadership. Effective manufacturing strategy can be viewed as securing one or more manufacturing/marketing positions where the enterprise exercises competitive leadership and superiority. A strong manufacturing research and product development capability is often essential if these specific objectives of leadership and superiority are to be attained and enlarged.

Among the defensive features of external flexibility, a variety of specific objectives can be established: for example, the numbers of independent technologies, customers, and market segments that are to be serviced. This type of flexibility objective strives to reduce the vulnerability of the organization to external contingencies, a certain number of which must be accepted and planned for as being statistically inevitable.

When the volatility of many technologies is recognized, a manufacturing strategy may be directed toward the development of manufacturing capabilities and product excellence in a number of loosely related technological areas. Similarly, the vagaries of all supplier-customer relationships frequently lead to the strategy of avoiding the establishment of manufacturing activities that would be dependent upon a few large customers unless favorable long-term supply contracts can be secured. More broadly, prudent manufacturing strategies are many times focused upon servicing a number of market segments, thereby compartmentalizing the potential risks of certain market segments being restructured or deteriorating. Inasmuch as even the largest industrial corporation is faced with resource limitations, these flexibility objectives may compete with and detract from the strategic alternatives of concentrating manufacturing resources for maximum effectiveness upon a more restricted number of apparently attractive alternatives.

The objective of internal flexibility—that is, strengthening the organization's ability to respond to contingencies—is focused primarily upon liquidity. Financial liquidity is a measure of the assets of a corporation that can be converted immediately or on comparatively short notice into cash on terms reflecting either their fair market value or their value to the corporation. Cash on hand and in banks and marketable government securities represent the most liquid assets, while certain in-process inventories of specialized products as well as plant and machinery often represent the least liquid types of assets. Because the most liquid types of assets generally offer the lowest rates of return, and vice versa, and the liquidity of investments in manufacturing activities is generally very low, an objective of high liquidity invariably conflicts with the objective of maximizing the market value of the shareholders' investment in manufacturing activities. The analysis of financial ratios offers several indexes by which the financial liquidity of an organization may be measured: the current ratio, the acid test ratio, the ratio of current assets to fixed assets, and the ratio of equity to debt. In view of the constraints that liquidity objectives may impose upon maximizing other near-term and long-range objectives, the strategy of manufacturing must exert a reciprocal influence upon the establishment of realistic liquidity objectives.

A measure of how swiftly plant and machinery could be converted to fulfill widely varied, alternate, or unanticipated manufacturing requirements without major and costly modifications may be described by the hybrid term "physical liquidity." Physical liquidity may be an important objective in the development of a manufacturing strategy. In evaluating a special-purpose, highly mechanized, high-volume, low-unit cost manufacturing process versus an alternative process characterized by less automatic general-purpose equipment resulting in somewhat higher unit costs, an organization emphasizing the objective of high physical liquidity would stress the advantages of the latter alternative.

The successful applications of increasingly automated equipment and manufacturing systems in new and continually expanding industrial fields elevate to greater importance the flexibility objective of physical liquidity. The strategy of manufacturing must investigate and define carefully the opposition and relationships between maximizing the flexibility of manufacturing facilities and maximizing other near-term and long-range objectives. Again, flexibility is rarely an additive attribute to manufacturing strategy but an objective that can only be satisfied at the cost of compromising other desirable objectives.

PERIPHERAL OBJECTIVES

This discussion has now examined the three dimensions of our general definition of manufacturing objectives: near-term objectives, long-range objectives, and flexibility. Prior to concluding this discussion of objectives, it is appropriate to acknowledge the presence of a variety of responsibilities and constraints and of peripheral objectives. A multitude of management programs and practices can be counted in this area: employee safety, education, training, health and welfare programs, more ambitious programs based upon management paternalism, union considerations and cooperation, legal responsibilities and constraints, and community obligations and civic participation. There is always the possibility of a misleading oversimplification. It appears, however, that such objectives fall into one of three categories.

First, many of these supposedly unique and noneconomic objectives in reality are only special cases of one or more of the three dimensions of our general definition of manufacturing objectives. For example, a manufacturer may emphasize the exceptionally high quality of his products, implying that this quality standard is an altruistic—and sometimes unrequited—contribution to mankind. In fact, this notably high standard of product quality may simply define the market segment being serviced, and the corporation quite likely could not compete effectively in other market segments where lower standards of product quality are expected.

Second, this category of objectives often represents little more than compliance with either legal requirements or the minimum standards of conscience and human decency. With reference again to the example of the manufacturer of products meeting exceptionally high standards of quality, it may be that any management of integrity and strong character could not even consider manufacturing a product of lesser quality that resulted in contaminant levels or performance faults that could endanger human safety, health, or life.

Third, this category of objectives may represent totally unjustifiable programs or practices that have been assumed to satisfy some ill-defined desire or philanthropic interest of management. Where there is no compelling, profit-contributing reason for their existence, and where they are absorbing management effort that should be directed toward achieving more rewarding objectives, these pseudo-objectives should be identified and removed immediately from the goals of management. Again, returning to our example of the manufacturer of products of outstandingly high quality, it may be that the consumer does not recognize, need, or even pay for this high standard of quality and that this quality standard is being maintained, perhaps unprofitably, solely to nourish the ego of management. This false quality objective should be banished immediately from the strategic manufacturing objectives of the enterprise, and management attention should be focused upon establishing a standard of product quality more compatible with market demand and acceptability. Thus such multifarious noneconomic objectives should be perceived in one of these three ways to avoid the introduction or perpetuation of sterile strategic objectives.

A discussion of the objectives of manufacturing cannot be concluded without acknowledging the influence of the objectives of individuals. It has been emphasized that an organization is composed of many persons, in their capacities both as individuals and as members of various subgroups, and that each person or group may have interests and objectives that conflict with those beneficial to the organization as a whole. Certain kinds of individual-organization conflicts seem to be characteristic either of smaller closely held corporations or of larger publicly held corporations; other conflicts of objectives may exist more commonly between the shareholders of the corporation and the professional managers with only a limited equity investment in the corporation.

An older management of a publicly held corporation frequently may assume an excessively conservative attitude toward risk; this attitude is symptomatic of an individual objective of maximizing the security of the present management rather than of maximizing more fertile manufacturing objectives. The older shareholder-managers in a small closely held corporation with a poor record of sales and earnings growth may emphasize the individual near-term objective of maximum current earnings and dividend payout to the detriment of the corporation while other near-term objectives, long-range objectives, and flexibility are ignored. An individual objective of social service and responsibility, while praiseworthy, can become an obsessive interest of management, frequently resulting in the dereliction of other responsibilities and the failure of the enterprise to secure basic manufacturing objectives. In many smaller closely held corporations, the purposeful creation of capital gains may be an individual objective of the shareholder-managers; while this objective is often subject to abuse, it can also complement the other organizational objectives of the corporation. Similarly, provision for estate liquidity can be an important individual objective in the smaller closely held family corporation; failure to provide this may not only emasculate the legitimate estate of a major shareholder but also jeopardize the ability of the enterprise to achieve other worthy manufacturing objectives.

Because even the largest corporation is an organization of people, the directive or expectation that the manufacturing objectives shall not be influenced by the aims and interests of individuals is unrealistic. On the other hand, a manufacturing strategy should recognize these individual objectives so that, where possible, they can be channeled toward the creative fulfillment of the corporation's manufacturing objectives and, where this resolution is not possible, they can be identified and isolated—if need be, forcibly—to preclude insidiously thwarting or weakening the progress of the corporation.

These diverse and often conflicting objectives can be assigned different priorities and can be combined in an almost unlimited number of ways to formulate an effective strategy of manufacturing. Historically, almost all industrial corporations have defined objectives concentrating their efforts within one industry or often within a segment of an industry. This policy has generally been effective and conforms to the basic strategic principle of concentrating forces to secure a specific objective with maximum effectiveness and certainty. It is interesting to observe, however, that the past decade has witnessed an increasing number of larger manufacturing organizations that have evolved an apparently effective strategy culminating in the conglomerate, multi-industry, or multimarket form of organization. This strategic process is often called heterogeneous diversification. Litton Industries, Inc., FMC Corporation, International Telephone and Telegraph Corporation, and Textron, Inc., are among the prominent manufacturers that pursue this type of strategy with marked success.

Having disposed of its last textile operations in 1963, Textron displays all of the characteristics of the contemporary conglomerate. With annual sales exceeding $1.1 billion, it encompasses 30 divisions organized into four product groups (aerospace, consumer, industrial, and metal) and manufactures products as diverse as rocket engines, toiletries, processed poultry, electronic instrumentation, and rolling mills. Recognizing that the corporation's primary objective is to earn a consistently high rate of return on the shareholders' equity in the enterprise, Textron's senior management has formulated a manufacturing strategy that exhibits many of the attributes of a holding company. Its resources are shifted both internally and externally into the manufacturing opportunities that fulfill this objective most effectively. The corporation's senior management exercises strategic and financial planning and control, while the autonomous divisional managements have virtually total authority over operational planning and control.

Textron's primary mode of growth has been to acquire established profitable manufacturing companies, often not the leaders in their industry but commonly possessing proprietary products; service operations have been avoided. In addition to its outstanding financial flexibility, Textron believes the conglomerate form offers maximum protection against production and product obsolescence in an environment that exhibits an accelerating rate of technological change. It has shunned narrow product identification and has pursued a manufacturing strategy directed toward advancing and expanding its technological competence in many traditionally unrelated industries.

Near-term objectives, long-range objectives, and flexibility are the three dimensions of our general definition of manufacturing objectives. The presence of individuals' objectives as well as of noneconomic objectives must be acknowledged, but these influences

64

must never be permitted to undermine or divert attention from defining and attaining the manufacturing objectives that promise to be most beneficial to the total organization. The geometrician who assigns excessive values to any one of the three dimensions of Euclidean geometry will generate grotesque forms; similarly, the industrial manager who gives undue emphasis to any one of the three dimensions of manufacturing objectives will develop an unstable and bizarre strategy of manufacturing.

Although the three dimensions of manufacturing objectives may be helpful categories for thoroughly analyzing and gaining a deeper understanding of these objectives, the pre-eminent objective of any manufacturing activity—and the one that fuses together all others— is to maximize the market value of the shareholders' equity in the enterprise. The specific and quantifiable fulfillment of this pre-eminent objective must be the aim and justification of every element of manufacturing strategy. Only when the manufacturing objectives of the enterprise have been identified and defined with precision is it possible to embark upon the development of a corporate strategy of manufacturing.

IV

Strategy

*The best strategy is always to be
very strong, first of all generally,
then at the decisive point . . .
there is no more imperative and
no simpler law for strategy than
to keep the forces concentrated.*
— Karl von Clausewitz

*Let the man who has to make his
fortune in life remember this
maxim: Attacking is the only
secret. Dare and the world always yields; or if it beats you
sometimes, dare it again and it
will succumb.*
— William Makepeace
Thackeray

T HE COMPARATIVELY RECENT introduction of both the word and the
concept of *strategy* into the management of industrial enterprises
appears to offer an exceptionally useful frame of reference for
planning, operating, and controlling manufacturing activities. Strategy is associated most strongly with generalship; that is, the science
or art of utilizing the resources of war with maximum effectiveness.
Since strategy and strategic planning are not yet wholly familiar or
accepted as primary functions of industrial management, it may be
well to explore the several meanings and implications of this
concept.

Strategy suggests the dexterous management of resources to surpass an adversary or to achieve an objective, the way in which resources are arrayed or assembled in both space and time, the
purposeful and regulated movement or evolution of resources, and
the changing of the position and intensity of resources vis-à-vis those
of an adversary. Although the politico-military origins and over-
tones of the concept do not always parallel the planning needs of
industrial management, this primary association of strategy can
offer a constructive orientation for the direction of manufacturing
activities.

Strategy implies objectives, an adversary, a hostile environment,
resource limitations, maneuver, discipline, organization, and combination. Politico-military strategy has been defined as the use of
engagements to attain the object of war. Strategy must be unified,
but it is usually discontinuous, constructed of actions or engagements that are discrete and nonlinear. Strategy can be defensive, but
its aggressive components are most common; it usually is directed
toward some change in the status quo—a quest for *victory*. Strategy
demands the highest managerial and intellectual qualities of decisiveness, strength of will, boldness, imagination, and reflection.

To sharpen our focus, the adjective *kinetic* may be introduced.
It suggests the action and interaction of forces to effect or change
the motion of masses. Kinetics is the physical science of forces
evoking change, of dynamics, of acceleration (plus or minus) rather
than velocity. Forces can be deterministic, statistically predictable,
or totally random. Both the internal behavior and the external environment of an industrial enterprise can be described as kinetic.
The industrial enterprise exists in a state of dynamic rather than
static equilibrium; its position and velocity change instantaneously
and nonlinearly in relation to all other forces and masses in the
universe.

Thus a kinetic strategy of manufacturing must be focused upon
movement, growth, and change. It must perceive its external environment in terms of objectives, adversaries, and competitive response; it must structure its internal behavior in terms of discipline,
maneuver, and resource effectiveness; and it must be directed
toward an enlarging strength and superiority rather than a petrified
and passive existence.

A number of helpful contributions have been made examining

the ways in which the principles and practice of politico-military strategy can and should be emulated beneficially by industrial management. Obviously, it would be inappropriate and even mischievous to conclude that the principles and practice of politico-military strategy are or should be congruent with the economic strategy of an industrial enterprise. Therefore, it is best to avoid indulgence in an interesting, nimble, but sophistic investigation of the parallelisms, divergencies, and oppositions between politico-military strategy and the strategy of manufacturing.

Is the management process of strategic planning synonymous with long-range planning? In some instances, the answer to this question is "Yes," but in most instances it is obviously "No." Although a sound strategic plan usually exhibits both near-term and long-range dimensions, most of the long-range plans that have now become rather fashionable are not truly strategic plans. Why? In practice, long-range planning is often little more than an extrapolation of today's activities, generally at a crudely selected rate of increase in volume and sometimes punctuated by the termination of a current activity and the possible introduction of some new activity. Long-range planning may be "long" in terms of time but frequently shallow in terms of timing, sequence, and imaginative maneuver. It is usually concerned with doing today's jobs faster or better, or with achieving higher output rather than with defining and doing tomorrow's jobs in new and creative ways. It is concerned with servicing today's markets with more of today's products rather than with perceiving the requirements and opportunities of tomorrow's markets. All too frequently, long-range planning emphasizes the frontal expansion of the status quo in a quest for survival rather than the sequential deployment and engagement of resources in a quest for manufacturing superiority.

RESOURCES

Strategic planning determines the ways in which manufacturing resources are to be acquired or developed, allocated, and employed most effectively in the economic and physical processes of transforming certain raw materials from one form into some other form of greater utility or value to society. A strategy of manufacturing establishes both the series of transformation gaps to be spanned and the combination or mix of resources that promises to span each of these gaps with maximum efficiency and effectiveness, cognizant always of the need for certain types of flexibility—for example, adaptability and resiliency. This series of transformation gaps defines both the near-term and long-range objectives of the enterprise. The pursuit of an aggressive strategy of manufacturing demands that the organization gain and maintain the initiative over its competitors in perceiving and bridging the series of transformation gaps leading to the manufacturing/marketing positions where competitive leadership and superiority can be exercised.

With this series of objectives defined, a strategy of manufacturing specifies how the resources to secure each objective are to be acquired or developed, allocated, and employed. Desirable objectives frequently cannot be secured with even the most sagacious development and deployment of the always limited resources of an enterprise or without placing the enterprise in a dangerously exposed and vulnerable position. Consequently, the construction of a strategy of manufacturing commonly requires the repeated restatement of the transformation gaps to be spanned until at least one combination of resources available promises to provide the means to secure these objectives. On the other hand, the imaginative construction and resolute execution of a strategy of manufacturing often employs sparse resources in uncommon ways to achieve formidable objectives. Both politico-military and industrial history present numerous examples of great objectives being secured through the bold and original employment of exceptionally limited resources.

It has been noted that a strategy of manufacturing is meaningful only as one of the dominant vectors of a total corporate strategy. Viewed in this perspective, it is separable and whole in somewhat the same sense as naval or air strategy are related to a total national or politico-military strategy. Manufacturing strategy can be distinct from, but not independent of, total corporate strategy. Although all the primary vectors of corporate strategy are interactive and exert reciprocal influences, total corporate strategy is often a melding of functional or possibly of task-product strategies. In many industrial enterprises, "value added by manufacture" is a substantial if not the major source of profit contribution and capital generation; thus it is both reasonable and useful to develop and implement a functional strategy of manufacturing to define and fulfill the total strategy of the corporation.

The product-market mix of every industrial enterprise is in a continual state of flux. Corporate strategy attempts to perceive the ways in which this product-market mix is changing or can be changed, thereby identifying new product-market opportunities. Once these product-market opportunities have been identified, corporate strategy selects the mix and disposition of available resources expected to take maximum advantage of these opportunities. Although it is sometimes suggested that the marketing aspects of corporate strategy tend to have an external bias and that the manufacturing aspects of corporate strategy tend to have an internal bias, this usually is an oversimplified conception of strategic planning. To select the most fruitful product-market mix, the strategy of manufacturing as well as of marketing must be equally aware of the external environment and the internal resources of the enterprise.

Viewed with the acuity of hindsight that invariably results in exceptional discernments, the demise in 1966 of Douglas Aircraft Company, Inc.—culminating in its acceptance of a merger with McDonnell Company in January 1967—offers a prominent case of the consequences of an inadequate strategy of manufacturing.

As is true in every instance of industrial reversal or crisis, the Douglas case is replete with convincing explanations of the cause of its difficulties. Among them were the combination of a substantially larger number of orders for its DC-9 aircraft than forecast; the introduction of four new aircraft models on the assembly lines almost simultaneously; a multiplicity of customer-prescribed aircraft configurations; prolonged delays in the delivery of critical components, especially of jet engines and landing gear, from suppliers due to the escalation of the Vietnam war; appreciably higher manufacturing costs than anticipated; unexpected shortages of skilled labor accompanied by increased training costs; excessive turnover of personnel and abnormal learning curves; and a recession-fearing economy plagued by severe credit restrictions. Although the remarkable acceptance of the DC-9 by the airlines plus the spirited growth of missile and space activities led to optimistic profit predictions through the early part of 1966, by midyear it became apparent that certain long-term strategic deficiencies were leading not only to monumental losses—$27.6 million for fiscal 1966 and

$13.9 million for the subsequent three-month period ending February 28, 1967—but also to an unacceptable financial position. Inasmuch as its principal competitors, Boeing and Lockheed, weathered the same external difficulties successfully, Douglas' inability to cope effectively with these conditions must be ascribed to strategic deficiencies.

The initial error in strategy was Douglas' failure to develop jet-aircraft manufacturing capabilities during the early 1950's. After a Herculean effort, and almost a year after Boeing's 707 aircraft entered commercial operation, the DC-8 was finally placed on the market. By 1967 the extraordinary development costs of this program still had not been fully recovered. Not only did this tardy entry into the jet-aircraft field adversely affect the company's technological stance and manufacturing competency, but also the massive development costs of the DC-8 program severely depleted the resources of the organization and left it precariously undercapitalized. In the face of these constraints, Douglas withdrew from the supersonic transport program in 1963. After losing the Air Force competition in 1965, the firm lacked the resources to develop independently an expanded or so-called jumbo subsonic jet transport comparable to the Lockheed C-5A or the Boeing 747. Thus Douglas, unable to assume a primary role in producing these two principal types of future aircraft, was forced to abdicate its former role of industry leader.

By 1965, the Douglas strategy had been revised reluctantly to ignore the great challenges of the longer-range future and to concentrate on those programs that could be achieved within the near-term future—the short-range jet aircraft (DC-9) and three so-called stretch models of the DC-8 (Super Sixty Series). These strategic objectives appear to have been appropriate to the company's current condition and the industry situation. They also offered the attractions of two immediately salable and popular product groups that could be expected to generate sufficient earnings to rebuild its capital position. Although these objectives were selected prudently, Douglas' manufacturing strategy failed to provide two critical resources. First, operational controls were inadequate, resulting in ineffective and unresponsive managerial direction; and second, capital resources (especially equity) were inadequate to cope with unanticipated, but not uncommon, development costs, delays, and increased working capital requirements for commercial inventories. Although both of these essential resources, control and capital, could have been acquired if planning had been enacted earlier— $75 million of 4.75 percent convertible subordinated debentures were eventually sold in July 1966—Douglas neglected to identify, evaluate, and act upon these fundamental elements of its strategy of manufacturing.

Once the combination of unforeseen difficulties began to mount in early 1966, these strategic deficiencies resulted in failure—initially to alert management to the presence of these portentous developments in sufficient time to prescribe effective corrective action and then to provide the managerial and financial capabilities to implement the appropriate corrective action. By the end of 1966, the only constructive strategic option available to Douglas was to merge with a compatible organization offering these two critical resources. As late as 1965, a superior strategy of manufacturing probably could have offered to Douglas the needed managerial control and equity capital, thereby avoiding the subsequent merger with McDonnell.

Stated in the simplest terms, a strategy of manufacturing is the selection of attractive and achievable manufacturing objectives followed by the establishment and execution of step-by-step programs to secure these objectives. The pre-eminent objective against which the urgency of each of these specific and sequential manufacturing objectives is to be measured is the maximization of the market value of the shareholders' equity in the enterprise. This definition coincides with the politico-military definition of strategy as the use of engagements to attain the object of war.

The establishment and execution of these step-by-step programs to secure the defined manufacturing objectives determine the ways in which the limited resources of the enterprise are to be acquired or developed, allocated, and employed. Although a hallmark of superior strategy is the selection of objectives that are both imaginative and achievable, a truly great strategy also exhibits thorough step-by-step planning, and subsequent execution, of resource development and deployment. Grand objectives are hollow if painstaking planning is lacking; conversely, the most exhaustive planning and spirited execution of a strategy of manufacturing are ineffectual if the objectives are either timorous or unrealistically ambitious.

A strategy of manufacturing can establish an objective of product development, or market development, or both. These three alternative objectives pose one of the most fundamental questions facing any industrial enterprise; its response to this question outlines its strategy of manufacturing and defines with considerable fixity the ways in which the resources of the enterprise are to be employed.

PRODUCT DEVELOPMENT

A strategy of product development is based upon the conscious development of new products utilizing (1) an existing technology, (2) a technology new to the enterprise but related to its present concerns, (3) a new and unrelated technology, or (4) a combination of these three primary alternatives. To cite a common example: A manufacturer of vehicular tires may choose to concentrate product development effort within the familiar technology of tire production; the consequent manufacturing strategy would be confined to the manufacture of vehicular tires to satisfy the requirements of present and possibly selected new markets. Or this manufacturer may choose to broaden product development efforts to encompass the technology of industrial rubber goods; the ensuing manufacturing strategy could include, in addition to vehicular tires, the manufacture of a long list of industrial products such as beltings, vessels, mechanical parts and accessories, building supplies, and automotive and aerospace components. Or this manufacturer may choose to expand product development efforts to exploit the loosely related technology of industrial or agricultural chemicals; this choice would suggest a multifaceted manufacturing strategy introducing, in addition to the preceding products suggested, an almost unlimited number of industrial or agricultural chemical products such as plastics, surface coatings, films or fibers, fertilizers, and pesticides.

The strategy of manufacturing can conceivably be based solely upon any one of the three alternative objectives, or upon a combination of the primary alternatives with variations, depending upon the intensity and scope of each objective. Proverbs in every culture —"Let the cobbler stick to his last" and "Never put all your eggs in one basket," for example—can be resurrected to support almost any one or any combination of these three alternative objectives. Although the development of products utilizing an existing technology

73

may be presumed to employ present resources and manufacturing capabilities most effectively, it may severely restrict product development opportunities or present a fairly high risk of technological obsolescence if the existing technology offers a notably narrow or precarious manufacturing base. On the other hand, the development of products derived from new technologies—especially those that may be loosely related to current manufacturing activities—can expose many new and attractive opportunities and at the same time dangerously overextend the limited resources and manufacturing capabilities of an industrial organization. At the risk of introducing a rigid generalization, it may be suggested that product development be confined to those existing technologies with which the enterprise is most familiar unless or until these technologies constrict the manufacturing resources of the enterprise or are confronted with the hazard of obsolescence.

Regardless of how extensive the undertaking may be, a manufacturing strategy of product development must encompass one or more activities clustered around a clearly defined axis and must be directed toward securing one or more specific manufacturing/marketing positions where competitive leadership and superiority can be exercised. The simplest and often the most successful strategy of product development is to concentrate all resources of the enterprise upon the development of a limited group of products which are based upon an existing technology where the possibilities of achieving and maintaining a position of manufacturing/marketing superiority and competitive leadership are judged to be comparatively high. However, if this type of manufacturing strategy is believed to be too exposed, vulnerable to competitive response, or susceptible to technological obsolescence, or if it is thought to underutilize available resources, then a broader and more complex strategy of product development may be founded upon new and more loosely related technologies that often call for large and costly investments in new and less familiar types of resources and manufacturing capabilities.

To draw upon our politico-military analogy, the broader strategy of product development offers the strengths of greater freedom of maneuver, an increased number of attack and response options, and even surprise, but it embodies the latent weaknesses of excessive diffusion of resources, more ponderous communications, and, possibly, an inability to establish superiority at all points of possible engagement. In the absence of any axioms by which the so-called right strategy of product development may be selected, it can be accepted and re-emphasized that any effective strategy of industrial management is dependent upon securing manufacturing/marketing positions where the enterprise exercises competitive leadership and superiority.

A kinetic strategy of product development must emphasize movement and fluidity. While the well-known Maginot Line complex may still have occasional adherents and applications in a politico-military strategy of defense, this orientation is totally alien to the activities of industrial management. Accepting the practical production requirements that product design must be frozen periodically, manufacturing research and product development must be in continual motion, probing deliberately for new avenues of advance toward carefully defined product objectives. A viable industrial organization is designed and directed to be mobile, to display an accelerating and purposeful movement; the inertia of an organization in motion is often one of its primary strategic strengths, as opposed to the vulnerability and potential dissolution of a static organization. A strategy of product development finds manufacturing research and product development in the van of the organization, with the responsibility for discovering or creating new routes of advance and, often, of selecting the near-term or tactical objectives promising to facilitate the continued advance of the enterprise.

MARKET DEVELOPMENT

A strategy of market development offers a very different range of manufacturing options, although an overlap into the areas of product development is not uncommon. Market development seeks ways in which, without major modifications or additions, the organization's present family of products and present technological and manufacturing capabilities can satisfy new markets or additional segments of existing markets. This strategic emphasis can assume a variety of forms, but it is not necessarily dependent upon the development of radically new products or types of products.

A strategy of market development can be directed toward enlargement of the market populated by the organization's present category of customers. Although market saturation may not be possible, legally permissible, or even desirable, a reasonable objective may be to secure a substantially larger share of an existing market. For example, a manufacturer of guestroom furniture for the hotel/motel market seeking to enlarge its share of this market may discover through market research that its products are not truly competitive because they fail to meet certain preferences or specifications of major potential customers. Comparatively minor changes in product design may overcome these product deficiencies and thereby open up areas of an existing market where the manufacturer was not previously competitive, or it may be necessary to display a willingness to modify or incorporate special product design features to satisfy the differing and specific requirements of each of several major potential customers. In each case, the development or enlargement of one's share of an existing market will affect the strategy of manufacturing.

Market development can also be directed toward the enlargement of the market represented by the enterprise as its own customer. In a multidivisional company, the changing needs of various divisions may offer new opportunities for manufacturing divisions to supply more of the component, subassembly, and product needs for these consuming divisions. In the case of the furniture manufacturer, the scope and profitability of the manufacturing activities may be broadened simply by performing a larger number of the upstream operations in the total production process. Without introducing any new technology, expansion of kiln capacity, turning equipment, or veneering facilities may enable the enterprise to supply more of its total product requirements economically. Although integrating backward is sometimes abused, resulting in the introduction or maintenance of manufacturing activities of dubious profitability, most medium-size or larger industrial organizations offer many economically attractive opportunities to meet in-process requirements internally.

Pursuing another strategic option, market development can be directed toward markets populated by new customers similar to the present categories of customers. Generally, this is an option to be developed after a satisfactory share of a familiar existing market has been achieved. However, a manufacturing strategy may schedule some exploratory or introductory activities to be initiated in these closely related markets quite some time before a desired position is expected to be secured in an existing market. To return to the case of the furniture manufacturer, it may be determined that the present hotel/motel market can be expanded to encompass the institutional furniture market: for example, living-room and bedroom furniture for school dormitories, furnished apartments, and nursing homes. A careful investigation of these associated markets will reveal the necessity of incorporating many changes into the specifications and configuration of current product designs, but it is unlikely that these modified products will call for technological or manufacturing capabilities substantially different from those already mastered. This manufacturing strategy will probably have to recognize and implement many minor product design revisions as well as new production scheduling requirements, inventory policies, supplier relationships, and even packaging and distribution practices.

Without embarking upon programs where the present family of products and present technological and manufacturing capabilities are grossly inadequate, market development can frequently be directed toward markets populated by wholly new types of customers. Although the establishment of consumer awareness and acceptance as well as of effective channels of distribution may present formidable marketing obstacles, this strategy may require very little that is new in production know-how. Once again, in the case of the furniture manufacturer this strategy of extensive market development could suggest the introduction of residential furniture, other types of institutional furniture (for restaurants, dining rooms, and conference rooms, and the like), or even office furniture. A similar strategy might suggest the production of case goods and wood components for other industries, for example, cabinetwork for the marine, television, and electronics industries.

Typically, this strategy of market development can begin to require more pervasive changes in product design and technology. If the goal of this strategy is to be limited to market development, vigilance must be exercised lest these market requirements be allowed to introduce or demand major expansions in product technologies and manufacturing capabilities. Again, the objective of a strategy of market development is to secure enlarged manufacturing/marketing positions where the present family of products and the present technological and manufacturing capabilities of the enterprise can command competitive leadership and superiority.

A strategy of manufacturing is rarely based solely upon a program of either product development or market development. It is common to select a mix of both types of development, although greater emphasis may be given to one than to the other. In the case of the manufacturer of vehicular tires, even if the product development effort is confined to the familiar technology of tire production, this strategy most likely will be accompanied by a program of at least limited development of the vehicular tire market. Similarly, the furniture manufacturer that pursues a program of developing a market populated by wholly new types of customers will frequently have to support this effort with a product development program of some magnitude. Granted that these two objectives often introduce conflicting demands for resource allocations, it is more useful to view them as two vectors which will be in equilibrium in a kinetic strategy of manufacturing.

Measured by the critical standards of sales revenues and earnings per ton of steel shipped, the Armco Steel Corporation is the leader of the steel industry. Its position has been secured through its continuing and conscious efforts to develop those steel marketing opportunities offering maximum profit potential. This market orientation is exhibited by two of the company's three profit-center organizations—the Metal Products Division, a fabricator of steel construction products—such as integrated wall and roof systems, pre-engineered buildings, and culverts—and the National Supply Division, a manufacturer and distributor of a broad line of oilfield products. One of Armco's primary strategic objectives has been to reduce its dependence upon steel as a commodity and to develop manufacturing capabilities to support effectively those steel-related product groups that offer superior penetration into consumer markets and substantial profit margins.

The superior strategy defines these sequential product development and market development objectives precisely and allocates manufacturing resources in ways that mutually reinforce each of these two objectives. It avoids both the sterility of static objectives based upon making more of today's products for today's markets indefinitely and the diffusion of too many objectives based upon doing too many things in too many places with insufficient or overextended resources.

Manufacturing strategy must at all times emphasize a concentration of resources to assure freedom of maneuver and maximum effectiveness in securing specific objectives but must shun an excessively narrow deployment of resources that would be vulnerable to a competitor's flanking attack or response. Product development and market development programs offer two primary strategic options; the emphasis given to each of these options and the ways in which they are interlocked are both dependent upon the present and potential resources of the enterprise as well as its current market positions vis-à-vis the positions of its competitors. Manufacturing strategy is not a field in which all or even a majority of the enterprises in an industry can excel or *win;* therefore, a superior strategy will be the one that blends these two strategic options in ways that are both truly realistic and demonstrably more imaginative than the parallel efforts of competitors.

A strategy for growth and change implies a striving for better manufacturing/marketing positions accompanied by and resulting in an improvement in resource strength. This strategy can be energized in one of three ways:

- Internal development and expansion.
- External diversification and acquisition.
- Some combination of these two alternatives.

The development of a manufacturing strategy will continually investigate and evaluate each of these alternatives, at the same time avoiding reliance upon oversimplified proverbs or industry rumors of dubious validity that might prejudice the objective consideration of an otherwise worthwhile alternative.

INTERNAL DEVELOPMENT AND EXPANSION

The internal development and expansion of the manufacturing resources of an enterprise quite logically is usually the first alternative to be considered. Regardless of how numerous or extensive the present deficiencies of any organization may be, it must possess some unique strengths, vitality, and personality to be in business. Therefore, the first step in the formulation of a manufacturing strategy is to identify these unique resources and to determine how these existing resources can be utilized—that is, developed and expanded—most effectively. A program of internal resource development and expansion takes maximum advantage of the apparently profitable investments already made in the organization's manufacturing activities, and enhances an established and seemingly accepted corporate personality.

For example, a small manufacturer of plastic housewares may not compare favorably with its larger competitors in the areas of minimum production costs or quality control, but it may possess a critical competitive strength in being able to respond swiftly to market trends and the desires of major customers. Obviously, although not neglecting other areas, a provident manufacturing strategy will seek to maximize this present resource and position of competitive superiority. The long-range strategy of the enterprise may suggest that other, possibly conflicting, objectives could be substantially more attractive than that of rapid turnaround time; in this case, the internal resource development and expansion program will schedule adequate control of these long-range manufacturing/marketing positions before relinquishing control of this present position of competitive leadership and superiority.

An objective appraisal of the manufacturing resources and critical strengths of an enterprise is the foundation of a sound strategy of manufacturing. This appraisal will discriminate between the existing resources that account for the organization's present position of competitive superiority and other resources that—although imbued with tradition and possibly venerated by some of the senior managers—do not significantly add to, and may even detract from, the organization's total manufacturing/marketing effectiveness. Once identified, the internal manufacturing resources and critical strengths capable of fruitful development and expansion will exert a primary influence on the selection of manufacturing objectives for the enterprise; reciprocally, these objectives will influence the ways in which existing resources are to be developed and expanded.

Although founded upon present manufacturing resources and critical strengths, internal development and expansion programs usually will not be restricted to present product or manufacturing technologies or to established market positions; rather, these programs will aim to employ current resources as a base upon which new and possibly loosely related resources and strengths can be founded. Undoubtedly, the implementation of this strategy will stretch the present talents of the organization and may demand the forced evolution of a new generation of products, the establishment of new types of manufacturing facilities, the design and installation of advanced processing equipment, and the employment and education of personnel with new skills.

Micro-electronics, concentrating primarily upon microwave and monolithic integrated circuitry, has been an important strategic component of Raytheon Company's internal development and expansion activities. An advanced mastery of this technology is viewed as essential to meet the continually more rigid performance, reliability, and configuration requirements of such important end-use customers as the Department of Defense. Enhancing its superior technological and product-line capabilities in the microwave and power-tube segment of the electronics industry, it has developed an integrated circuit limiter for microwave applications capable of sustaining one kilowatt peak power. Significant accomplishments have been achieved in the development of large-scale integrated circuits, many of which offer attractive commercial production and marketing applications. The corporation has developed and manufactures over 100 different types of diode-transistor logic (DTL) digital circuits in various configurations as well as linear (analog) devices and has achieved commercial production of a broad spectrum of transistor-transistor logic (TTL) very high-speed digital integrated circuits. A major manufacturer of electronic components as well as systems, Raytheon constantly examines the role of micro-electronics in meeting its manufacturing objectives, emphasizes manufacturing research and the development of micro-electronic circuitry benefiting both the components and systems operations, and pursues a strategy of manufacturing that strives to avoid conflicts or imbalance between these two activities.

The manufacturing strategy based upon the internal development and expansion of present resources and strengths will assess the potential of each of these assets, project these against the present and potential assets and the anticipated moves and responses of competitors, and relate these evaluations to forecast manufacturing/marketing opportunities. This type of strategic analysis can reveal the present manufacturing resources and critical strengths that warrant development and expansion, the most promising step-by-step internal development and expansion programs to be undertaken, and—quite importantly—the present assets that fail to justify major resource investments.

The most potent strategy is expressed where existing assets and talents exert the greatest leverage or multiplicative effort. This kind of strategy builds upon past accomplishments, maintains the integrity—and simultaneously enlarges the personality—of the organization, and is often self-correcting in avoiding a too rapid assimilation of new assets and talents. It is a rare, although certainly not unknown, situation where the internal development and expansion of present manufacturing resources are not a major—if not the primary—feature of a strategy of manufacturing.

EXTERNAL DIVERSIFICATION AND ACQUISITION

It is common to find that the potential of existing manufacturing resources is either insufficient to secure manufacturing/marketing positions where competitive leadership and superiority can be exercised or incapable of securing desired positions within specified time limits. This situation may be met in an enterprise when the manufacturing resources are exceptionally weak or depleted, the manufacturing resources have little carryover into new technological or market areas to be exploited, or financial or marketing resources are notably stronger than manufacturing assets and talents. In these cases, a program of external diversification and acquisition may become an important, perhaps even a dominant, feature of a strategy of manufacturing.

External diversification and acquisition programs are a way of *buying* some manufacturing resource or critical strength in which the organization is deemed to be deficient. These programs may buy manufacturing facilities, distribution channels, market position, skilled personnel, or proficient operating management; frequently, *time* is the most precious resource to be procured. Although the phenomenon has only recently been recognized and subjected to critical examination, a sufficient number of excellent contributions have been made in the field of corporate diversification and acquisition to preclude the need for a prolonged discussion of the many problems that may be encountered. However, an acquisition is essentially a corporate graft rather than a growth; perhaps the analogy of a corporate graft to an organic graft would not be inappropriate. When carefully investigated, skillfully prepared, and joined and nurtured under salubrious conditions, a graft can result in an organism of substantially improved characteristics, strength, and vitality. The rejection of either body, on the other hand, will cause failure of the graft, immediately or within a short period of time, resulting in the loss of the implanted body and the weakening, and occasionally the loss, of the main body. Excessively large grafts or an excessive number of grafts performed in rapid succession will produce at best a strange structure and quite commonly will exhaust the main body resulting in a total system that is stunted, if not destroyed.

External diversification and acquisition programs can be an aggressive—even a daring—manufacturing strategy when an enterprise needs manufacturing resources it does not currently possess and cannot develop economically. However, in view of the many hazards and potential problems associated with diversification and acquisitions, the strategic objectives leading to this type of program must be defined with special precision and pursued dispassionately. A program of internal development and expansion may later prove to have been ill-advised or misdirected; although it could represent a wasteful use of resources, it would seldom precipitate corporate disaster. Regrettably, a program of external diversification and acquisition that led to similarly disappointing results quite likely could also lead to the extinction of the acquired body as well as to the infection and even debilitation of the main body. The most ambitious and imaginative manufacturing strategies will frequently embody some major features of external diversification and acquisition, but these programs will be adequately balanced with sound programs of internal development and expansion.

Manufacturing strategy can be compared with football strategy: A passing (aerial) attack may be analogous to a manufacturing strategy that emphasizes external diversification and acquisition, while a running (ground) attack may be analogous to a manufacturing strategy that emphasizes internal development and expansion. A superior professional football team will exhibit a strategy drawing upon both options, although player resources and competitive responses will influence the ways in which each of these strategic options can be implemented and emphasized for maximum effectiveness. External diversification and acquisitions can offer an excellent route of swift strategic advance, often yielding superior forward positions, but this same route of advance may result in overextended lines of supply and communication, dangerously exposed flanks, inadequate internal control, and an unstable disposition of scarce resources.

An acquisition is rarely a bargain; consummated improvidently, emotionally, or in excessive haste, it can easily become mutually depressing and an unproductive resource investment by the surviving organization. On the other hand, an acquisition preceded by careful analysis and planning and undertaken with enthusiasm and conviction can secure an otherwise unattainable objective and can represent a creative resource investment. It is likely that external diversification and acquisition will fulfill some role—in numerous cases, an important role—in an aggressive strategy of manufacturing.

Manufacturing strategy determines the ways in which manufacturing resources are to be acquired or developed, allocated, and employed with maximum effectiveness. A kinetic strategy for growth and change may emphasize the options of product development or market development, or a balanced combination of both of these options. Activation of this strategy will be through the internal development and expansion of manufacturing resources, or the external diversification and acquisition of manufacturing resources, or—most frequently—the thoughtful intermingling of these two types of actions. Of course, the operational objective of manufacturing strategy is to secure one or more specific manufacturing/marketing positions where competitive leadership and superiority can be exercised; the pre-eminent objective of manufacturing strategy is to maximize the market value of the shareholders' equity in the enterprise.

V

Economics

When we review what goes on in the world, is it not evident that in all human transactions the caprices of fortune turn wisdom into jest.

—Tacitus

Uncertainty and expectation are the joys of life. Security is an insipid thing, though the overtaking and possessing of a wish discovers the folly of the chase.

—William Congreve

T HE SCIENCE OF economics is concerned with the production, distribution, and consumption of goods and services, the generation and uses of income, wealth, and material resources. It is concerned with monetary values and relationships, with costs and prices, with sources of supply and intensities of demand, with investment opportunities and competitive environment, and with the optimum mix of the factors of production—labor, land, capital, and technology. An industrial enterprise is primarily an economic organization; it is established and exists for the specific purpose of fulfilling some requirement of society for which there is an economic demand. Therefore, a strategy of manufacturing is essentially a program to enhance the economic vitality and the competitive strength of an enterprise through the most profitable development and deployment of its manufacturing resources.

Tactically, it is usually possible and invariably prudent to forecast and evaluate fairly precisely the anticipated economic performance of near-term manufacturing activities. Contemporary techniques of return on investment analysis, profit planning, and control budgeting permit ongoing and near-term operations to be planned and controlled with an adequately high degree of realism and effectiveness.

These forward planning techniques, however, are often of limited value—and can even be grossly misleading—in the area of strategic planning. Manufacturing strategy is directed toward creating new competitive relationships, developing new products, exploiting new technological capabilities, and serving new markets. Thus past experience and historical data are seldom meaningful, while quantitative forecasts of future expectations are fraught with uncertainty. Inevitably, the economic dimensions of manufacturing strategy are based upon order-of-magnitude predictions of trends, capital requirements, labor content, operating input costs, and market demands. As is true in almost any worthwhile endeavor, superior craftmanship is always to be desired; however, the success of a manufacturing strategy is commonly due to the recognition of pertinent economic factors and influences rather than to computational precision.

An efficacious strategy is always dependent upon the selection of an appropriate objective. Ideally, an appropriate objective is one promising a high probability of success; one where the organization can maintain mastery and competitive superiority but also one which requires reasonable organizational growth if success is to be assured. The selection of a modest or inconsequential objective can result in the dissipation and uneconomical employment of the organization's resources, while the selection of too ambitious an objective can result in defeat or disaster or, at best, only a Pyrrhic victory. A fundamental economic dimension of a strategic objective is a measure of market demand.

DEMAND ANALYSIS AND FORECASTING

For a well-established product or market, industrial economics offers several useful techniques—for example, regression analysis—for predicting future demand. These techniques appear to offer rather precise numerical answers, but generally they cannot cope with the unknowns of new technological developments or structural changes in the market. Their effectiveness is usually limited to near-term forecasts of market demand.

Manufacturing strategy is concerned with the generation of change, the creation of new products and new types of products, the development of new technology, and the exploitation of new marketing opportunities. The common techniques of forecasting economic demand are seldom valid in the field of strategic planning. If change is to be wrought, the future will not be a simple extrapolation of the past. Consequently, more imaginative, courageous, and much less precise techniques of forecasting demand must be employed. In other terms, a strategic forecast of demand must be based upon a *functional* rather than a *technical* market analysis.

The economic analyses preceding the decision of General Motors Corporation to commit $52 million to establish automobile assembly facilities in Brazil were primarily functional market analyses. In recognition of the fact that the total automobile market in the United States appears to be stabilizing at about 10 million new units per year—whereas the foreseeable market outside the United States can be predicted to expand to 13 million new units per year—25 percent of General Motors $3.7 billion three-year total capital expenditures program to expand and modernize facilities during 1964–1966 was invested outside the United States.

Brazil is one of the selected nations that appears to offer an acceptable socio-economic environment and an adequate potential market to support large-scale automobile assembly operations. However, the decision to undertake the Brazilian program was based not upon sophisticated projections of operations, profit contribution forecasts, and return on investment analyses, but primarily upon demand analyses indicating that the automobile market in Brazil offers substantial potential growth and upon management's conviction that General Motors will participate in this growth profitably. A similar rationale underlies most imaginative strategic decisions to establish new manufacturing facilities or capabilities, especially in international commerce; for example, in 1967 Texaco Inc. announced the construction of a 100,000-barrel-a-day oil refinery in Ghent, Belgium, to yield a full range of petroleum products—liquified petroleum gas, naphtha, jet fuels, motor gasolines, diesel fuel, waxes, and heating oils—for European distribution.

A functional demand analysis seeks to identify and evaluate the causes of market evolution. A functional analysis reveals existing demand that is unstable or deteriorating, indicates potential demand that is not presently being satisfied, and discovers shifts in demand and new demands that can be exploited or accelerated. It suggests gross limits of the anticipated magnitude, intensity, and continuity of this potential demand, and appraises its vulnerability to invasion by both parallel and substitute product development programs. Market demand is probed for totally new products resulting from new manufacturing capabilities as well as byproduct development. On the other hand, the recognition of new market demands also establishes priorities and magnitudes of resource investment in specific manufacturing research and product development programs. Functional demand analysis investigates the causes and the demand vectors of trends, predicts market structure in the meaningful long-range future (usually about 5 to 10 years), and suggests order-of-magnitude dimensions for the significant segments of this future market.

COST-OUTPUT FUNCTIONS

Demand analysis is a technique of forecasting total revenue or income, usually under an array of different price schedules. The ultimate measure of economic effectiveness, of course, is not gross revenues but net profit. Since the most ingenuous definition of profit is that which is left over after deducting all costs from total revenues, manufacturing strategy must be founded upon a realistic appraisal of the costs of each alternative course of action. Again, although tactical planning can usually draw upon a wealth of accounting data and historical costs to construct a fairly precise representation of the immediate future, strategic planning must avoid the temptation simply to project historic costs into the fundamentally different environment of a more distant and uncertain future.

Cost analyses supporting a strategy of manufacturing must commonly construct cost schedules for the production of new products and new types of products. These cost schedules must usually examine a variety of methods of manufacture and several scales of operation. The most challenging aspect of strategic cost analysis is technological forecasting. Anticipated breakthroughs in both product technology and manufacturing technology not only exert a primary influence on strategic timing but also introduce a high degree of uncertainty into strategic cost analyses. Even when the definitional lack of precision in strategic cost analysis is acknowledged, it is still essential that these analyses be undertaken as thoughtfully as possible to identify the cost parameters of each alternative course of action as well as the factors currently subject to the greatest uncertainty. Perception rather than precision is the foremost requisite of strategic cost analysis.

The essential behavior of cost-output functions, under both near-term and long-range conditions, is a classic consideration of industrial economics. Near-term costs are those incurred over a period of time of sufficient duration to vary output by altering product (variable) costs in relationship to committed and managed (fixed) costs. The near-term costs are based upon a time period and cost structure for which the more inflexible factors of production—for example, structures, primary equipment, and management—are constant in quantity and configuration. Thus both total costs and unit costs are only a function of product (variable) costs. Near-term costs are those exhibited by any ongoing operation where plant and management have already been established and are not subject to major variations; they are also exhibited in a forward planning analysis when a specific combination of plant and management is under examination. One plant-management combination will display cost-output functions quite different from those of another plant-management combination representing a significantly larger or smaller scale of operations.

For a specific combination of plant and management, industrial economics offers the generalized cost-output relationship presented in Exhibit 1. Classically, it is assumed that committed and managed costs are fixed and that product costs are a function of output. Exhibit 2 indicates the generalized relationship of product costs and unit costs. Product costs are those costs required to produce each successive unit of output, and may often be called marginal costs, incremental costs, or unit variable costs. It is most common for product costs per unit of output to decrease somewhat after a mini-

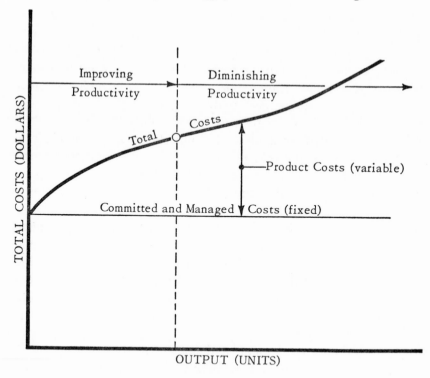

EXHIBIT 1
GENERALIZED NEAR-TERM TOTAL COST FUNCTION

mum scale of operations is achieved; however, after an optimum scale of operations has been passed, the product costs per unit of output increase, often fairly rapidly, because of the inefficiencies resulting from overloading the facilities of production. Optimum (minimum) average product cost per unit of output is achieved when increasing output forces the incremental product costs to a level equal to average product cost (A); most significantly, optimum (minimum) average total cost per unit of output is achieved when a further increase in output forces the incremental product costs to a level equal to average total cost (B). Therefore, optimum (minimum) average total cost per unit of output is achieved at a level of output substantially above the level where minimum incremental product cost is realized.

Long-range costs are those incurred over a period of time of sufficient duration to vary output by altering *all* costs; that is, all

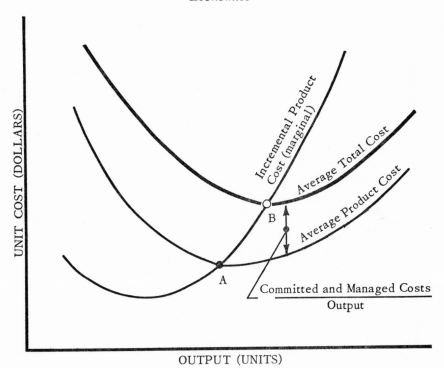

EXHIBIT 2
GENERALIZED NEAR-TERM PRODUCT COST AND
UNIT COST FUNCTION

of the activity's costs are variable and no factors are fixed. Although long-range costs are a function of the scale of operations as well as the mix of all factors of production, an important role of long-range cost analysis is to explore total costs as a function of the scale of operations, assuming that the optimum mix of the factors of production has been determined through a sequence of near-term cost analyses. Industrial economists have undertaken many interesting studies to construct long-range cost functions based upon historic performance records for a number of stable basic industries—and even very large industrial organizations—where adequate data are available for many sizes of plant.

The generalized long-range cost-output relationship is presented in Exhibit 3. The long-range cost curve—often called the "planning curve"—is constructed tangent to a sequence of near-term average

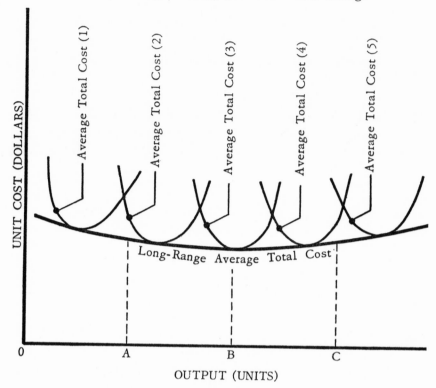

EXHIBIT 3
GENERALIZED LONG-RANGE UNIT COST FUNCTION

total cost curves $(1, 2, 3 \ldots n)$ that are previously determined for all reasonable scales of operation. Thus the long-range cost analysis reveals the variation of cost with output allowing all factors of production to vary freely in quantity and configuration, thereby suggesting optimum plant location, capacity, technology, and operational standards. This type of analysis identifies for each scale of operation the most economical production function and cost structure. It should be noted that there is a different near-term average cost curve for every possible throughput level and technological configuration (production function); the result is an entire family of near-term cost curves, each enveloped by and representing a discrete point on the long-range average cost curve.

Even though theoretical, the construction of long-range cost-output functions can reveal a number of other useful insights and relationships. It is characteristic for long-range average costs to be reduced as the scale of operations is enlarged due to the increasing economies of size; of course, it is then characteristic for these costs ultimately to rise because of the diseconomies of overextended distribution and administrative control. It is also especially interesting to note (Exhibit 3) that the long-range average cost curve is tangent to the near-term curves at only one point; further, this point of tangency is to the left of the minimum-cost point for all near-term functions falling to the left of the long-range minimum-cost point and to the right of the minimum-cost point for all near-term functions falling to the right of the long-range minimum-cost point. Only for the optimum near-term cost curve 3 are the near-term and long-range minimum-cost points coincident. Thus for outputs less than *OB*, for which curve 3 represents the optimum cost-output function, it is more economical to underuse a somewhat larger plant operating at a volume lower than its minimum-cost output than to overuse a smaller facility—the output *OA*, for example, would be produced more economically by the plant represented by cost-output function 2 than by the smaller plant represented by cost-output function 1. Conversely, if output from one plant must exceed the optimum level *OB*, it is more economical to overuse a somewhat smaller plant than to underuse a larger facility—the output *OC*, for instance, would be produced more economically by the plant represented by cost-output function 4 than by the larger plant represented by cost-output function 5.

These theoretical principles of industrial economics offer a framework for undertaking strategic cost analyses. Based upon historic experience, such cost-output relationships are the most commonly anticipated relationships. Their principal use in strategic planning is to structure a complex and an often amorphous situation, thereby helping to reduce the degree of uncertainty characteristic of this type of analysis; it is not expected that this type of strategic cost analysis will yield quantitative values of precision or certainty.

In consideration of the unsatisfactory margins of the general bakery flour market and the expectation that the economic patterns of this industry would not improve within the foreseeable future, strategic cost analyses supported the decision of General Mills, Inc., in June 1965, to contract its flour milling capacity and to curtail its sales of specification bakery flour. In the year following this decision, the company closed 9 of its 17 flour mills and accepted a decline in bakery flour sales in excess of $70 million; during this period, similar strategic cost analyses led to discontinuing the production and sale of refrigerated biscuits and other specialty dough products, resulting in closing four plants. However, while total sales in the fiscal year 1966 were only $524.7 million, compared with 559.0 million in fiscal 1965, total earnings per common share increased from $2.65 to $3.07; and net profits on sales increased from 3.6 percent to 4.4 percent.

In conformance with General Mills' manufacturing strategy of concentrating resources and efforts in the areas offering the most attractive returns, strategic cost analyses commended a capital expenditures program for plant and equipment in 1966 totaling $41.6 million. The principal features of this program were the erection of the corporation's first package foods plant at St. Charles, Illinois, designed specifically to meet the requirements of the food service and baking industries, and the completion of new cereal and snack production facilities at West Chicago, Illinois, and Lancaster, Ohio. Thus, objective economic evaluations led to the divestment of numerous manufacturing activities which, although traditionally the foundation of the company's business, failed to generate adequate earnings; concurrently, strategic cost analyses revealed the attractive profit potential of both existing and new families of consumer and commercial food products, and positive steps were taken to establish the manufacturing capabilities to supply these types of products.

ASSUMED CERTAINTY, RISK, AND UNCERTAINTY

Forward planning analyses can be made under (1) assumed certainty, (2) risk, or (3) uncertainty. Many types of long-range, as opposed to strategic, planning analyses can be made assuming that our comprehension of the future is complete and subject to no significant doubt. The acquisition cost, stream of earnings, redemption price, and rate of return on a United States Government bond provide a classic example of a forward planning analysis made under assumed certainty—although a forecast of the future market value of the bond is an analysis made under uncertainty. Similarly, the evaluation of alternative types and capacities of prime energy converters, turbines, generators, transformers, and switchgear for an electric power station is another common example of an analysis often made under assumed certainty. In practice, very few strategic planning questions can be analyzed validly under assumed certainty.

An analysis made under risk perceives a limited number of possible futures; the probability of each of these possible futures occurring can be defined with adequate statistical precision. To establish the probability of each future occurring with a satisfactory degree of reliability, sufficient historical records of past performance or similar data must be available or must be generated. A classic example of an analysis made under risk is the determination whether or not to insure against a possible loss. Other familiar examples of planning tasks pursued under risk are analyses of queueing processes and preventive maintenance programs. Inasmuch as analyses made under risk demand data sufficient to establish a realistic probability of each future occurring, strategic planning analyses rarely fall within this category.

Strategic planning analyses are almost always made under uncertainty. This type of analysis perceives many futures and acknowledges that the probability of each or of any of these futures occurring cannot be stated with any precision. The economic behavior of any contemplated strategic course of action is dependent not only upon the future market demand (volume) but upon price schedules, input costs (for example, wages, raw materials, and supplies), the responsive strategy of competitors, and many other kinds of speculative data. Confronted with data of such uncertain validity, is it even possible to evaluate the economic dimensions of a manufacturing strategy with an adequate degree of reliability and usefulness?

The traditional way to cope with this dilemma, if not to resolve it, is to approach these analyses as deterministic problems; that is, analyses to be made under assumed certainty. Specific values may be selected for all input data—for example, sales volume will be 6,750,000 units in FY-3 and 7,100,000 units in FY-4 and average total costs will be $3.37 per unit in FY-3 and $3.29 per unit in FY-4; the analysis is then pursued with the tacit assumption that the probability of this future's occurring is unity. Then, since it is recognized that the true probability of this exact future's occurring is quite low and perhaps negligible, subjective factors called variously irreducibles, nonnumerical data, or judgment are introduced and evaluated in reaching an action-decision. Frequently, the objective input data are so uncertain, and these subjective factors are such an important part of the analytical process, that the final decision is essentially a subjective one, the initial operational and financial analyses having been little more than an interesting but tangential exercise.

Several interesting techniques of evaluation are currently proffered for analyses to be made under uncertainty. One technique is founded upon the dominance principle: Any alternative that, even in an uncertain future, will be superior to another alternative in the face of all conceivable eventualities should be selected in favor of the second alternative. The principle of insufficient reason (Laplace principle) assumes an equal probability for all futures; therefore, the future with the maximum expectation is to be selected. The rather conservative or pessimistic maximin (or minimax) principle selects the alternative that maximizes the minimum profit (or minimizes the maximum cost). Displaying a less conservative bias, the Hurwicz principle introduces a subjective "index of optimism" to identify the most attractive alternative. Finally, the minimax regret principle (proposed by L. J. Savage) selects the alternative that minimizes the maximum regret.

Each of these techniques of evaluation is of interest to the operations analyst and may be employed beneficially on occasion to structure strategic planning analyses. However, the inability of these techniques to represent the vast number of intermediate alternatives and to project vividly the kaleidoscopic futures of an enterprise often tends to limit their usefulness and their acceptance for strategic planning.

SIMULATION

Present-day computers frequently enable simulation models to be constructed and subsequently manipulated to examine the forecast economic performance of a manufacturing strategy under a broad array of possible futures. A marketing strategy may suggest a specific pattern of growth in sales volume for a product, and the primary operational and financial analyses of alternative manufacturing resources and technologies to produce this product will be based upon this market forecast; however, supplementary analyses may be presented for growth in sales volume perhaps at rates 5, 10, 15, 25, and 40 percent less than the forecast, as well as at selected rates greater than the forecast. Similarly, the primary analyses will be based upon a specific pattern of future price schedules and input costs; supplementary analyses can be presented for each of these groups of input data—singly and in various combinations with other input data—varying at rates other than those forecast (for example, wage rates may be examined increasing annually at a rate of 2, 3, 4, and 5 percent). These analyses reveal dynamically the breakeven points of a contemplated activity as well as the sensitivity of net profit and cash flow to the responsive strategies of competitors for each of the possible futures selected.

Once the primary analyses have been undertaken and the simulation model has been programmed for computer processing, it is a simple and economical step to make an almost unlimited number of supplementary analyses examining the contemplated manufacturing activity under all reasonable economic conditions and eventualities. Although it is possible to design computer analyses to explore a multidimensional continuum of all possible futures, management judgment can usually reduce the scale of these analyses substantially and without any loss of usefulness by selecting those groups of discrete futures warranting investigation. Summary printouts can present and compare in a concise format the critical measures of economic performance—for example, sales volume, net profit, cash flow, and return on investment—for each possible future; supporting detail statements can provide expanded data for each case warranting more careful examination.

The use of simulation models to investigate the economic characteristics of a manufacturing strategy (while essentially quite simple) can offer several important advantages. First, it recognizes many futures and recognizes too that the probability of each or any of these futures occurring cannot be stated with precision or assurance. Second, it measures the sensitivity of the strategic activity to certain critical economic conditions and eventualities and identifies the many possible futures to which the project is relatively insensitive. And finally, rather than being a passive technique of analysis, it acknowledges and encourages the influence that the enterprise and the contemplated strategy should have on the future by displaying the combination or groups of combinations of input factors that can be expected to result in superior performance.

This type of strategic analysis can acknowledge and correlate the uncertainty of both input data and predicted performance. In recognition of the inherent uncertainty of estimates of future economic conditions, the strategic simulation model seeks not one crisp answer leading to an automatic decision but a selected array of output data with which to construct the topography of the future. Since the topography of the future can be constructed with a high degree of certainty and realism, the information can be generated with which to chart a sound strategic course into this future with a correspondingly high degree of reliability and usefulness.

SENSITIVITY ANALYSES

The economic evaluation of a manufacturing strategy should be focused upon the sensitivity of total profitability and return on investment to each of a substantial number of uncertain environmental factors. These sensitivity analyses seek to identify those environmental factors to which the profitability of the contemplated strategic activity would be most vulnerable and thereby strive to reduce the inherent uncertainty of these factors if at all possible, to incorporate adequate reserve resources into the strategic activity and so render it comparatively invulnerable to these factors, or to discard the contemplated strategy in favor of an alternative strategy less sensitive to these environmental factors. For example, profitability is extremely sensitive to raw material prices for manufacturing processes where value added by manufacture is small in relation to the cost of raw materials. The profitability of an enterprise engaged in the manufacture of rigid plastic packaging is extremely sensitive to the price of plastic resins, the major input factor. The enterprise might seek to reduce its vulnerability to raw material price fluctuations by investigating the alternative manufacturing strategies of developing its own capability to produce plastic resins, entering into an appropriately flexible long-term supply contract with a major producer of plastic resins or developing new product groups characterized by substantially greater value added by manufacture and consequently less dependence upon the price of plastic resins.

It is often useful to develop graphic analyses of the sensitivity of a contemplated strategic action to each of the pertinent environmental factors. Some of the factors warranting analysis are variations (from the primary forecast) in sales volume, sales price schedules, pattern of sales buildup, total capital cost (as well as working capital requirements), dominant input costs, and the economic life of the activity. Other factors that are usually of lesser importance are variations in interest rates and the cost of capital, methods and periods of depreciation, and the impact of any investment tax credits.

Exhibit 4 illustrates the sensitivity of a contemplated strategic activity's profitability to variations in sales volume (on the assumption that all other factors remain constant). For example, if sales volume should follow a pattern 25 percent lower than the primary forecast, the anticipated rate of return would fall about 10 per-

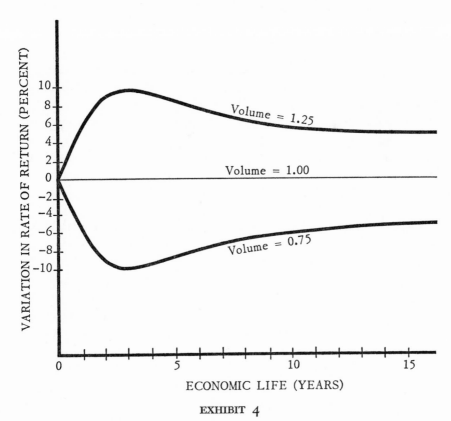

EXHIBIT 4

Variation in Rate of Return Versus Sales Volume

centage points below the forecast rate of return at a three-year economic life and about 6 to 8 percentage points below the forecast rate of return if the economic life of the activity should be extended (as anticipated) to about 10 to 15 years. Similar graphic analyses can be developed for each of the other significant factors to reveal the factors to which profitability is especially sensitive as well as those to which profitability is comparatively insensitive.

CAPITAL BUDGETING AND STRATEGIC PROFIT PLANNING

It has been emphasized that the pre-eminent objective of a strategy of manufacturing is to maximize the market value of the shareholders' equity in the enterprise. Although the market value of the shareholders' equity in a manufacturing activity is the result of many interacting influences, the economic performance of the activity is unquestionably an influence of paramount importance. Anticipated economic performance can be investigated most effectively by undertaking return-on-investment analyses. With the aid of simulation techniques, return on investment analyses of contemplated manufacturing strategies can be an incisive way of identifying not only the most attractive alternative but also the sensitivity of investment profitability to both favorable and unfavorable situations. These techniques provide the tools with which to introduce into a strategy of manufacturing the two economic components—capital budgeting and strategic profit planning.

Capital budgeting is concerned with the identification, evaluation, and selection of superior investment opportunities; the detailed planning, implementation, and control of these expenditures can properly be viewed as a critical part of the capital budgeting process. The capital budgeting process is commonly the way in which the manufacturing strategy is energized; it is the process by which all strategic and operational elements are evaluated and integrated into a strongly focused manufacturing endeavor and the process through which the commitment and deployment of major resources are made. Too often, performance objectives based upon return on investment are handicapped by the necessity for otherwise satisfactory current performance to be related to an excessive, uneconomic, inflexible, or unimaginative capital investment base. A manufacturing strategy can be deemed effective only if the always limited resources of the enterprise are engaged with maximum effectiveness and efficiency. Overly cautious or sloppy investment analysis and capital budgeting result in the commitment of excessive resources, thereby failing to provide the opportunities for the most attractive investment returns in the future.

Strategic capital budgeting can be enhanced by the use of simulation models to explore the sensitivity of both total capital cost, including working capital requirements, and return on capital investment to all pertinent environmental factors. Even for such manufacturing strategies as advanced state-of-the-art activities that are permeated with uncertainty, these economic evaluations can be extremely useful in determining order-of-magnitude forecasts and at least gross limits for anticipated performance. The probabilistic nature of strategic capital budgeting often suggests that no capital should be committed until a realistic and fully adequate "capital investment authorization" has been made to support completion of the endeavor, even if the most unfavorable possibilities are encountered. The capital investment authorization will represent the total of committed, programmed, and reserve resources. As the capital investment process progresses, and factors are transformed from an uncertain to a budgeted and ultimately to a completed status, the capital investment authorization will be continually redefined and, in most cases, reduced. In the general situation where various strategic activities are being initiated concurrently, it is unlikely that all of these activities will encounter the most unfavorable possibilities; therefore, several activities may have a partial claim on the same reserve resources.

This capital budgeting procedure encourages the practice of planning, implementing, and controlling strategic manufacturing investments with all possible precision and efficiency; more importantly, it acknowledges the high degree of uncertainty attendant to most strategic activities, does not attempt to subject them to the same limitations as routine operational investments, and assigns adequate reserve resources to avoid aborting an otherwise creative strategy of manufacturing by inadequate financing.

Although capital budgeting may initiate the commitment of resources to a strategic manufacturing activity, the analysis of these investments must be supported by a strategic profit plan. Strategic profit planning differs from annual profit planning and control budgeting in that it is related to a period projected substantially further into the future; it is usually aimed toward the creation of new manufacturing activities rather than toward a one-year extrapolation of present activities and, consequently, is based upon forecasts subject to significant re-evaluation as year-to-year operational profit planning is undertaken. However, to be meaningful, strategic profit planning must exhibit the same penetration, diligence, and craftsmanship demanded of annual operational profit planning; otherwise, the strategic planning process is thwarted, and the performance standards upon which a strategy of manufacturing is founded may lack credibility.

The capital budget and the strategic profit plan are complementary; the capital budget defines the magnitude, timing, and purposes of each capital expenditure, while strategic profit planning defines the operational characteristics and performance standards of the activities energized by these capital investments. In concert, these two budgetary techniques define the predicted and then the actual economic effectiveness and profitability of a manufacturing activity.

The effective development and use of these budgeting techniques are demonstrated by the Minnesota Mining & Manufacturing Company. A general objective of this corporation is to maintain an annual sales growth rate of 10 percent and earnings before taxes of 20 to 25 percent on total sales as well as net worth. The corporation actually employs three budgets—an operations budget, a cash flow budget, and a capital expenditures budget. The operations budget is essentially a strategic profit plan developed in full detail for the ensuing year and realistically for the next five-year period; this budget presents marketing and manufacturing objectives, the strategy to secure these objectives, and the costs of all inputs to implement this strategy. The cash flow budget is, of course, a monthly schedule of cash receipts and disbursements for purposes of monetary planning and control. The capital budget is a quarterly schedule of capital expenditures for the next three-year period.

Within the framework of the total corporate budget and strategic criteria established by senior management, these profit plans and capital budgets are constructed by divisional management, evaluated by each group vice president, and then consolidated by the corporate controller. Each division's budget as well as the total corporate budget is subsequently subject to a final and penetrating examination, occasional revision, and ultimate approval by a senior management budgeting committee; because a majority of the directors are members of this committee, budget acceptance invariably constitutes approval of the board. Although next year's forecast performance is an immediate consideration, the strategic planning defined through these budgets is of increasing importance at each higher level of investigation and approval. International economic appraisals influence and often revise internal planning.

The preparation of these formal budgets follows a specific annual schedule; nevertheless, strategic profit planning and capital budgeting make up a continual process. The formal budgets are reviewed and revised whenever warranted by internal developments or changes in external conditions. Despite the emphasis given to quantitative analyses and statistical forecasts, 3M emphasizes that the most meaningful assurance of satisfactory budgetary performance is frequently the resolution and enthusiasm of divisional managements.

Contemporary techniques of profit planning recognize two general types of budgets for operational planning and control—the product-cost, or contribution, budget and the committed- and managed-cost budget. A primary distinction between these two types of budgets is that the committed- and managed-cost budget is predominantly the legacy of past strategic decisions, whereas the product-cost budget —although subject to some constraints because of past strategic decisions—reflects either the proficiency or the ineptness of operating management. In view of the dominant influence of past strategic decisions upon current profit plans, it can often be claimed with validity that return on investment is neither an equitable nor a responsive way to evaluate periodically the performance of operating management. By definition, operating management rarely participates in or is responsible for the development of manufacturing strategy. Therefore, it is to be preferred that operating management be held accountable for the product-cost budget and that return on total investment be the responsibility of that senior management group charged with the formulation of strategy.

Careful examination of the operating statement or the forward profit plan for most manufacturing enterprises reveals the disproportionately large influence of past strategic decisions upon any one period's performance, in contrast to the more limited areas of performance improvement and control to which operating management has access. This characteristic is most pronounced for manufacturing activities that employ highly mechanized or automated facilities. Not only can the capital investment in these facilities be substantial, thereby increasing the ratio of committed costs to total costs, but also many costs that formerly were truly variable product costs tend to become managed costs. In many automated operations, for example, direct labor no longer constitutes a product cost that is a function of output; it is a comparatively fixed managed cost, fluctuating only through quantized states that often depend simply upon whether the plant is to operate at all or whether it is to operate one, two, or three shifts. By increasing the ratio of committed costs to total costs, two strategic objectives are usually sought:

- Total costs per unit of output at the forecast levels of operation are expected to be substantially lower than for alternative methods of manufacture.
- The increasing ratio of fixed costs to variable costs (especially labor) makes the operation less sensitive to the increases in these variable costs that have played an important part in the long-range inflationary bias in our total economy.

The magnitude and the fixed nature of many capital investments in manufacturing activities, coupled with their increasingly dominant influence upon future operating performance, emphasize the importance of evaluating as fully as possible the economic dimensions of alternative manufacturing strategies.

QUALITATIVE CONSIDERATIONS

The economic components of manufacturing strategy are faced with an apparently irreconcilable dilemma. By definition, strategic planning is concerned with the purposeful creation of change and, consequently, must be founded upon the most vague and uncertain economic input data; on the other hand, the cost of error in strategic planning is almost always extraordinarily high and, on occasion, can be overwhelming. Obviously, these opposing considerations are simply the stuff of strategy, the reasons why strategy formulation commands the finest talents of analysis and judgment on the part of industrial management and, consequently, seldom yields to pre-scribed techniques of resolution. However, the probability of suc-cess can be enhanced by identifying and investigating thoroughly each of the salient economic factors that may influence the strategy of manufacturing.

Strategic objectives must first be defined with whatever degree of precision is possible and evaluated in quantitative economic terms. Generally, an aggressive strategic objective is amplified with thoughtful forecasts of sales volume, price schedules, and demand elasticity; a defensive objective may be amplified by comparing economically the maintenance of a secured market position with alternative courses of retrenchment if manufacturing capabilities fail to advance and expand in response to an anticipated competitive challenge. Although the uncertainty of the data upon which strategic demand analyses must be founded will usually result in a rather broad range of possible futures, these analyses can establish order-of-magnitude limits on market expectations and reveal the relative soundness or precariousness of a contemplated strategy. Frequently, strategic cost analyses can then explore the anticipated cost-output relationships for all reasonable mixes of the factors of production and various scales of operation. Even when these cost analyses are unable to suggest an adequately narrow band of cost-output func-tions, they can be invaluable in identifying the areas of critical uncertainty, and their magnitude and impact upon the total cost structure. Finally, the matching of market and cost analyses leads to the profit analyses of a manufacturing strategy. Ultimately, a strategic marketing objective is selected that will lead to a superior profit objective; strategic manufacturing objectives can be the mile-stones and, often, the primary resources to achieve the specified goals. The most careful analysis of market demand and cost-output functions is invariably essential to reduce the opposition between the uncertainty of all strategic forecasts and the extraordinary high cost of strategic error or failure.

The realism and usefulness of primary market demand and cost-output analyses can then be enlarged many times through the use of simulation models. These analytical techniques enable industrial management to interrogate the model, to receive quantitative re-plies, and to explore the most likely economic performance of a manufacturing strategy when faced with any conceivable internal or external deviation from the primary plan. These analytical techniques can examine the sensitivity of the indexes of economic performance—such as sales volume, net profit, cash flow, and return on investment—to the favorable and unfavorable factors that may influence each possible future. Once maximization of the shareholders' equity in the enterprise is accepted as the pre-eminent objective of a strategy of manufacturing, return on investment analyses is frequently the closest approximation that can be made of the degree of success with which alternative strategies can be expected to meet this objective. Even though substantial imponderables may have to be acknowledged, simulation techniques to evaluate return on investment can accentuate the conditions under which the success of a manufacturing activity may be anticipated as well as any less propitious conditions; if the manufacturing strategy is subsequently to be implemented, management then is alerted fully to the conditions that must be created or maintained to assure its superior economic performance.

However, it must be recognized that the nature of manufacturing strategy may often limit the impact of even the most careful economic analyses. It will be recalled that, in our previous investigation of objectives, many of the most important objectives would have to be strictly classified as noneconomic. Frequently, a rigorous economic analysis of the most imaginative or forceful strategies would result in information of questionable value; economic analysis will always be subordinate to sound intuition and strategic perception. An organization insisting that all manufacturing activities of a strategic character be fully justified economically at inception will either forgo many strategic opportunities of outstanding merit or foster the presentation of deceptive analyses—a practice that can be debilitating when carried into the operational evaluation of ongoing and near-term manufacturing activities. Although the economic dimensions of any contemplated strategy of manufacturing must be investigated thoroughly and every reasonable effort must be exerted to define its economic characteristics, a preoccupation with analytical sophistication or comprehensiveness should not be permitted to dull the vision and boldness of a creative strategy. Rate-of-return analyses projected into the calculable future do not lead invariably to the maximization of the market value of the shareholders' equity in the enterprise.

VI

Animation

A MANUFACTURING ACTIVITY CAN and should be viewed in a variety
of ways. Our previous discussion has surveyed the ways in which
a manufacturing activity can be viewed and measured as an economic activity. Quite commonly, manufacturing operations are
viewed as insensate physical facilities, structures, mechanical devices, automata; our subsequent discussion of automation will examine certain aspects of this concept.

Our investigation now will view the total manufacturing system
as an organism—a complex of sources of supply inputs, machines,
accessory facilities, personnel, technological expertise, management,
money, and channels of output distribution—that exhibits coher-

ence, adaptability, and an independent vitality. The manufacturing organism can be a department, a plant, a division, or the dominant activity of a manufacturing enterprise. Irrespective of the scope of operations, a manufacturing activity is truly an organism if it can be viewed as something more than a simple machine to be acquired, placed in operation, and run according to predetermined directions for a certain economic life. The manufacturing organism is not a repetitive mechanism but a viable endeavor exhibiting growth, reproduction, adaptability, and initiative—that is to say, the attributes of life.

The composition of biological as well as social organisms can be reduced to elements that are essentially inorganic. Similarly, the composition of the manufacturing organism is largely inanimate—machines, processing equipment, buildings, utility services, computers, and vehicles. Although human intelligence and imagination can breathe life into this inorganic complex, the process is not necessarily inevitable or natural. There are countless manufacturing operations which, although nominally subject to human direction and control, can scarcely be viewed as viable organisms. The attributes that animate a manufacturing activity are entrepreneurial curiosity and foresight, managerial vigor and resolution, and technological innovation, ingenuity, and creativity (to a much lesser extent because of its innate scarcity). Human intelligence and imagination introduce the highest animating force into this organism through the formulating of a kinetic strategy of manufacturing.

Manufacturing is an activity to be viewed, never in a state of completion or perfection but always in the process of forced evolution. Manufacturing strategy is the aspect of intelligence that imparts consciousness and purpose—movement and direction—to the total organism. It is the animate force that perceives the long-term requisites for the organism's survival and growth and subsequently adapts and develops the organism to meet these requisites. A strategy of manufacturing formulates the direction of advance and deploys the necessary resources to support this advance; it infuses the manufacturing organism with both intelligence and energy. Animation is a quality transforming a manufacturing activity from a static mechanical operation into an evolutionary social force. Thus we return to one of our definitions of the manufacturing function: It is the social function of generating change.

CONTINUAL FOMENTATION

A strategy of manufacturing continually seeks to foment changes in the product-market mix. This activity is focused upon both the development of new products and the exploitation of new market opportunities. An awareness of product potentials and new product capabilities can broaden existing markets and foster the development of wholly new market areas. Similarly, an awareness of either active or latent market needs and dissatisfactions can lead to continuing and purposeful product redesign and evolution as well as to the creation of new product families. If the initiative is taken to force continuing and constructive changes in the product-market mix, the manufacturing resources of the enterprise can be constantly deployed and enhanced to secure or to strengthen product/service superiority in carefully defined markets. An imaginative strategy of manufacturing will strive at all times to keep the product-market situation in a state of controlled turmoil, imbalance, and tension, not to stabilize a product-market mix. Although there is no paucity of examples of excesses leading to corporate and even industrywide confusion and chaos, manufacturing activities must be stimulated incessantly in the quest for manufacturing/marketing positions where competitive leadership and superiority can be achieved. The abuse and misuse of the word *dynamic* has blunted much of its meaning and effectiveness; nevertheless, *dynamic* is one of the few words capable of conveying the concept of a product-market mix as being in a state of unceasing flux and evolution.

A strategy of manufacturing also seeks to foment changes in both product and production technology. Again, technology in the manufacturing organism must be viewed not as mechanical cleverness or ingenuity, but as the physical manifestation of management's concept of the industrial enterprise. It may not be possible or prudent for every manufacturer to occupy the rather glamorous frontiers of scientific development and technological creativity; nevertheless, every manufacturer does have the opportunity to exercise technological innovation and adaptability. In most industries, survival and growth demand that some substantial phase of a manufacturer's operations display technological superiority; for example, certain noteworthy and recognizable technological capabilities may be characteristic of the product line, or the manufacturing technology may be capable of high-volume output at attractively low unit costs, or the manufacturing technology may be unusually responsive to customer service requirements through rapid completion of orders or the ability to handle special orders and product configurations. Product and production technology are seldom stationary; the initiator of technological change is the animated manufacturing organism rather than the complacent observer who must inevitably scramble to duplicate or mimic—usually a little too late—the technological achievements of his more spirited competitors. If it is acknowledged that technological change and breakthroughs do not "just happen" and are rarely the results of accident or good luck, then the responsibility as well as the opportunity to create technological change become more urgent. Often, a manufacturer's technological capabilities can be an outstanding resource and competitive strength.

Most fundamentally, a strategy of manufacturing seeks to foment changes in the socio-economic environment and to adapt swiftly to those socio-economic influences it did not instigate. A legendary example of both initiating and adapting to socio-economic changes is the difference in the manufacturing and marketing strategies pursued by the Ford Motor Company and General Motors Corporation in the mid-1920's. On a large scale, both of these organizations at different times and in different ways have brought about extensive socio-economic changes. Irrespective of the scale of operations, however, every manufacturer must incite change in the socio-economic environment; this change may be to satisfy or create a demand for new types of products, for wider variation in existing products, for products exhibiting different quality/reliability standards, or to develop certain product groups in totally new markets.

The animated manufacturing organism devotes its primary energies to generating (as well as adapting to) socio-economic change rather than to the routine management of internal operations; it perceives itself as an active and responsible instrument of social change and, hopefully, betterment; its efforts are directed toward (1) recognizing and then (2) satisfying or overcoming significant social and economic needs or dissatisfactions. A manufacturing strategy strives to develop and engage the manufacturing resources of the enterprise in ways that will accelerate socio-economic change and yield maximum satisfaction and rewards to society as well as to the manufacturer. This goal is neither noble nor altruistic; it is simply a recognition that in any transaction both the producer and the consumer must realize a profit.

STRATEGIC AWARENESS

Thus a pre-eminent management function in an industrial enterprise is to think and plan strategically. New product ideas, the development and expansion of existing product families, and the introduction of new products often constitute the first area in which a manufacturing strategy is formulated. *Product strategy* demands intimate cooperation between the functions of marketing and manufacturing. But manufacturing management can be especially creative and visionary in developing new product ideas that could seldom occur to either consumers or marketing management. Although cases abound of superb new products that could be readily manufactured but required years to develop an adequate market, many successful products have been created by an inventor or manufacturer in response to no measurable market demand and without the encouragement of a favorable market analysis.

In-depth market studies can determine what it is the consumer wants, and a product can then be designed to meet these consumer-oriented specifications, yet many of the most exciting and successful new product ideas have resulted from producer creativity rather than consumer dissatisfaction. The consumer is seldom dissatisfied until a producer presents a superior product, thereby producing a new standard of comparison and dissatisfaction with the previously available products.

The sagacious pursuit or creation of new technological opportunities is another element of strategy to be formulated by the manufacturing organism. Some technological proficiency is inevitably displayed in any manufacturing activity; this proficiency can range all the way from the work of the tinkerer or resourceful mechanic through more imaginative automated facilities to advanced state-of-the-art achievements emanating from the most sophisticated research and development efforts. Industrial management first identifies the strengths of its current technological proficiencies and evaluates the competing technological influences that present the most serious external threats, then charts a course by which existing technological proficiencies can be reinforced or expanded or essential new technological proficiencies can be developed. A superior manufacturing strategy need not be founded upon the most advanced or complex technology; however, it must be based upon an awareness of the consequences and direction of technological development, a forecast of meaningful technological change, and a plan by which the enterprise can continue to exploit either present or newly acquired technological capabilities. For any industrial enterprise in which the role of manufacturing is of more than secondary importance, the deliberate evolution and exploitation of technological opportunities is an essential element of manufacturing strategy.

Finally, the management of an industrial enterprise will think and plan strategically in terms of manufacturing capabilities. Manufacturing capabilities encompass all the various kinds of physical facilities and human resources that together constitute a manufacturing organism. The energies and resources of the enterprise must be directed toward developing these manufacturing capabilities in ways that will meet the three, often competing, goals previously discussed—near-term objectives, long-range objectives, and flexibility. The satisfaction of these differing objectives frequently suggests the establishment of capabilities of a type, quantity, and quality in excess of immediate requirements. These capabilities are to be developed, not to assuage the possible paranoia or egoism of management, but to assure the successful accomplishment of specific corporate objectives, always with maximum economy or cost-effectiveness. The viability of the manufacturing organism is measured best by gauging its ability to grow, to survive adversity, and to reproduce; its ability to perform current operations successfully is an indication only of existence, not of vitality.

Although technological forecasting is fraught with imponderables, one of the more fertile technologies in 1966-1967 appears to be the development of filament or fiber composite materials—for example, metal-matrix composites embodying high-strength fibers, popularly called fiber-reinforced metals. Several materials possess tensile strengths on the order of a million pounds per square inch when produced in the form of small-diameter (approximately one mil) fibers or "whiskers" of extraordinary perfection. Because these whiskers are minute single crystals, virtually devoid of dislocations or stress-concentrating flaws, their unprecedented strength is achieved, not by the comparatively low stress required to induce a dislocation through a crystalline matrix, but by the necessity of simultaneously breaking many atomic bonds. The strength of a metal-matrix composite is established by the strain that can be accepted by the fibers without fracturing, inasmuch as the matrix deforms plastically because of its ductility after being stressed beyond its yield point.

The most promising fine fibers for metal composites appear to be graphite whiskers, silicon carbide whiskers, alumina whiskers, iron whiskers, silica fibers, carbon steel wire, boron filaments, carbon fibers, stainless steel wire, tungsten wire, and beryllium wire. Although their very high cost now limits any consideration of fiber composite materials to specialized aerospace applications where their exceptionally high strength-to-weight ratios are essential, many forecasts suggest that these materials offer an important potential for broad industrial applications after the formidable problems of fabrication are overcome.

The technology of fiber composite materials is a promising component of manufacturing strategy for several companies that recognize this opportunity. The General Electric Company pioneered in the production of sapphire whiskers for material reinforcement in its space sciences laboratory in 1959. Along with Avco Corporation, Monsanto Company, Texaco Inc., and United Aircraft Corporation, General Electric is also developing and producing boron filaments. The Carborundum Company is now producing silicon carbide whiskers, and Union Carbide Corporation has achieved commercial production of continuous carbon filaments; both these manufacturers are also producing silicon-carbide-coated graphite as well as higher strength carbon fiber. Union Carbide's commercially produced THORNEL 40 graphite yarn combines a filamentary modulus of elasticity (stiffness) of 40 million pounds per square inch with a density of only 0.056 pounds per cubic inch, yielding a specific modulus of 715 million inches (in contrast to boron's specific modulus of only 610 million inches). Inasmuch as stiffness is a paramount property in the filamentary reinforcement of plastic resins, the combination of this exceptionally high specific modulus with a tensile strength of 250,000 pounds per square inch offers entry into a broad application spectrum for fiber-reinforced composite materials. In developing competence in the technology of fiber composite materials, each of these manufacturers is employing the strategic resources of product development, advanced technology, and exceptional manufacturing proficiency.

Operational management is charged with the responsibility of "doing today's jobs better." However, a strategy of manufacturing is first concerned with defining the kinds of jobs that must be done five, ten, or more years from now. It is concerned with filtering transient from significant changes in product-market mix, in product and manufacturing technology, and in the socio-economic environment. A strategy of manufacturing is concerned with constructing vivid and realistic models of the manufacturing enterprise at various points in the future; of the environment in which this organism is to operate; and of the actions to be taken by the enterprise continually to grow, reorganize, and adapt itself to meet these future objectives effectively. Although the principles of biological evolution have been grossly misapplied and abused, the manufacturing organism can draw upon some of these principles for guidance. The chronological scale of industrial evolution is more foreshortened than those known in biological evolution; thus the evolutionary process is quite visible, and the efficacy of alternative ways of growth, reorganization, and adaptation is known relatively swiftly, albeit often too late for the affected organism.

EVOLUTION

Organisms adapt to their environment through the integrating agencies of selection, hybridization, inbreeding, and mutation. Each of these modes of organizational evolution can be employed in formulating a strategy of manufacturing. A fundamental distinction between biological and industrial evolution is that the biological organism reacts to external influences nonconsciously, whereas it is presumed that the manufacturing organism can foresee its future and adapt consciously in the most effective ways to meet this anticipated environment. Biology offers no parallel to planned or forced evolution. In the 20th century, however, almost all social, economic, and political agencies are committed to some form of planned or forced evolution. Industrial management—at least within its own sphere—usually acknowledges the inevitability of both internal and external change and the urgency of actively forecasting, adapting to, and exploiting change rather than passively reacting to change after its accomplishment. Animation is the quality infusing the manufacturing organism with intelligence—foresight and vitality— to impose its influence upon the environment, both present and future, rather than quiescently submitting to external influences.

If tomorrow's jobs can be anticipated and defined with some degree of certitude, this intelligence will exert a major influence upon the planning and execution of today's jobs. The dimensions of time and direction can then greatly extend the mission of each manufacturing activity. Today's jobs are to be viewed as elements of maneuver and advance rather than as operational tasks, as the first step of a continually evolving strategy rather than the latest step of operational perfection, as the commencement rather than the consummation of corporate growth. Together with today's facilities, they are to be planned to meet the carefully defined needs of tomorrow as well as the immediate requirements of today. A strategy of manufacturing must suggest milestones and delineate the character of the manufacturing activities, the types of physical resources, and the job profiles and skills that are to be achieved as each milestone is passed; this strategy will then establish the specific actions to be taken and the resources to be developed as each milestone is met. The anticipation and definition of tomorrow's jobs again emphasize the crucial role not only of technological forecasting but of judicious socio-economic forecasting.

Although academic research is refining analytical techniques, and both government and private sources are improving data collection, correlation, and dissemination techniques, strategic forecasts must invariably be based upon the perceptive interpretation of this voluminous data and the imaginative use of the techniques of analysis. Numerical analysis provides the essential inputs—but seldom the final answers—with which to forecast and define the jobs of tomorrow.

Once the importance of these technological forecasts is recognized, many strategic questions are revealed in terms of the location, configuration, capacity, capabilities, technological sophistication, and life span of investments in manufacturing resources—facilities, research and development, personnel, and management. An active program of overt industrial intelligence will be drawn primarily, not from the activities of direct competitors, but from all technological and socio-economic activities and developments that could affect the manufacturing industries. It is sobering to note that in the past —and this is one trend that will certainly continue, if not accelerate, in the future—most long-term competition and industry realignments have been the result of factors outside a specific industry rather than the actions of direct or traditional competitors. Copper is not competing primarily with other copper smelters and fabricators but with aluminum, various alloys, and plastics. The office equipment industry has been revolutionized by the technology of data processing and information storage-retrieval. The long-range competition facing a cement producer is the technological progress and new product applications being achieved by the petroleum, chemical, steel, gypsum, and other building material manufacturers rather than the activities of other cement producers.

The socio-economic environment is broad, not only in terms of impinging technologies but also in terms of changing social organization and international influences. Survival together with the instinctive need to grow demands that the animated manufacturing organism be continually sensitive to these changes in its total environment; through internal adaptation and reorganization, these external changes become sources of competitive strength rather than the agencies of extinction.

SYNERGY

The analogy of synergy—a physiological phenomenon which may be defined as the cooperative, reinforcing, and often amplifying action of two or more organs, drugs, or stimuli—has been employed to describe the behavior of manufacturing organisms. Synergy usually implies that the net gain, accomplishment, or output is significantly greater than the arithmetic sum of all inputs. Synergy is displayed by the manufacturing organism when the combined effect of new and existing product groups, new and existing facilities, new and existing technologies, or new and existing productive capabilities is substantially greater than the arithmetic sum of these activities individually.

Essentially, the manufacturing strategist is seeking combinations where the addition of resource R_2 with value 10 to resource R_1 with value 10 will result in an effectiveness value—of not 20 but perhaps 25 or 30. A superior strategy of manufacturing will always seek to develop, acquire, and deploy resources in ways to maximize the synergistic action of this complex of resources and the effectiveness of the total organism. Not only is synergy a desirable goal to enhance total profitability but, as manufacturing activities expand, often it is also an essential characteristic if the organism is to retain its agility and balance and to avoid becoming clumsy and distended.

Among the various types of synergy that can be achieved, sales synergy is the most common. It can be displayed in several ways. A new product group can be introduced that complements or expands an existing family of products so closely related that substantially increased sales are secured with virtually no increase in selling effort and cost. Or new product groups may be acquired or existing product capabilities broadened so extensively that the manufacturer is viewed as being a full-line rather than a specialized producer; thus substantially increased sales result with only a modest increase in selling effort and cost. Or the acquisition and development of new product groups may provide so-called piggyback entry of existing product groups into markets where the manufacturer was formerly unable to gain admittance; again substantially increased sales result with only a modest increase in selling effort and cost. Manufacturing strategy strives to establish product development and market development programs that provide the maximum level of sales synergy. Without sales synergy, a proliferation of new product groups and capabilities can lead to an enervating diffusion of selling efforts and to bewilderment and confusion among consumers.

Investment or resource synergy is achieved when the effectiveness of existing resources can be enhanced markedly, or when the effectiveness of a combination of resources is appreciably greater than the arithmetic sum of these resources individually. A manufacturing facility equipped to accommodate several product groups rather than only one or two, a number of product groups processed or fabricated on common production equipment employing common tooling or common components, manufacturing research and product development yielding multiple benefits to various manufacturing activities, or central inventories of raw materials supporting quite diverse manufacturing operations illustrate some of the ways in which resource synergy can be displayed. In the more routine cases, synergy may be achieved through the improved utilization of resources; in the most imaginative cases, synergy results in a true multiplier effect upon the output of a resource. In one sense, synergy is synonymous with the economies of scale that provide the rationale for most major industrial expansions, mergers, and consolidations. A strategy of manufacturing is invariably concerned with ways in which resources may be developed and combined to achieve a synergistic effect.

Operational synergy is another common phenomenon. It is observed when support services and overhead costs are limited but distributed over an expanding base, when procurement can take advantage of large-lot economies, when common learning curves can be enjoyed, when physical distribution realizes higher load factors, and when facilities and personnel are engaged at close to full capacity. Although operational synergy is occasionally considered to be the province of the industrial engineer, the primary accomplishments (or deficiencies) in this area are the result of strategic action-decisions. Competent industrial engineering can assure the superior performance of a well-conceived operation, but it can seldom transform an ill-conceived operation into a profitable endeavor. In some ways, operational synergy is synonymous with operational efficiency; however, operational efficiency will usually be disappointing if the operations are disadvantaged strategically. A conscious search for and recognition of those conditions fostering operational synergy is a crucial responsibility in formulating a manufacturing strategy.

Synergy can also be displayed in the management of the enterprise. Inasmuch as the number of competent managers is always limited and invariably less than desired, special attention is to be given to maximizing management synergy. Usually, this objective can be satisfied by a strategy in which newly encountered management problems will not be too dissimilar from those where current mastery is being displayed. This admonition would suggest that a large-volume continuous process manufacturer consider with extreme caution and reservations a proposal embodying job lot or batch operations. Similarly, a manufacturer engaged in the production of precision aerospace equipment will approach with reluctance and introspection any program suggesting the production of variants of this equipment for the construction industry, where totally new product specifications, quality/reliability standards, production schedules and controls, and customer service requirements are to be met. Obviously, it is difficult to conceive a manufacturing strategy where management will not have to gain mastery in a number of new and unfamiliar situations, nor is an animated management likely to remain satisfied without these challenges. The critical consideration is that management exposure to and acceptance of significantly different situations be controlled—perhaps self-paced—and that an indigestible diet of new types of manufacturing problems, irrespective of their challenge and stimulation, be avoided.

Operational (on-stream) synergy as well as introductory (start-up) synergy may be displayed. In certain cases, competence may exist in both situations; it is more common to find only meager or even no competence in one situation or the other. Operational synergy can be realized by continually achieved cost economies; improved plant utilization; common and more efficient channels of distribution; or increased revenues through extended product capabilities, adaptations, and variations. Operational synergy can seek to allocate overhead and manufacturing burden over an enlarging base and to maximize the economies of scale.

On the other hand, introductory synergy can be realized in a new product-market development or acquisition through the maximum utilization of existing management experience and proficiency, of existing manufacturing facilities and capabilities, of existing technological and product design talents, or of in-house know-how and productive skills. Introductory synergy is usually achieved most successfully by an organization with some recent experience in new product-market ventures or in facilities start-up; however, foresight and careful planning can often compensate for the purported advantages of experience in this area. Although it is desirable to achieve both operational and introductory synergy, a thoughtful appraisal of the enterprise's special proficiencies and past accomplishments in each of these fields should strongly influence the formulation of a manufacturing strategy.

Manufacturing synergy may be directed toward amplifying and animating the productive skills and resources of an enterprise. This phenomenon may be most obvious in the area of hardware. With a modest increase in investment, facilities and equipment can often incorporate substantially increased performance characteristics, leading to a multiple expansion in capacity, flexibility, or quality/reliability standards. Facilities and equipment acquired for byproduct manufacture or for finished product variation frequently result in a disproportionate increase in sales revenue and income contribution. When designed and selected judiciously, facilities and equipment embodying performance characteristics in excess of immediate requirements can foster the development of critical new talents and capabilities, frequently yielding attractive returns within the meaningful future. Synergy will be achieved whenever an incremental investment in hardware can be expected to effect an appreciably greater improvement in total performance.

Various combinations of personnel talents and skills may also result in manufacturing synergy. Facilities and equipment are inert without the requisite design, operational, testing, and maintenance skills. Increasingly automated plants may result in diminishing the role of on-line operatives and operational skills, yet at the same time they upgrade the skill content of the design, testing, and maintenance forces. Especially in the latter areas, synergy can be achieved through the cross-pollination of talents between normally autonomous operations. The talents that accomplish outstanding product or facilities design in one area can often be directed toward comparable accomplishments in other operational areas; testing techniques and quality control standards may be extended to all operational areas after a noteworthy breakthrough has been achieved in one operation; normal, preventive, and extraordinary maintenance programs can improve levels of effectiveness and efficiency throughout an organization once one operation has established a superior program. Synergy will be exhibited both by the interchange of personnel with special talents and skills within an organization and by purposeful programs of personnel development, education, and job retraining.

Mutually reinforcing organizational capabilities may also display manufacturing synergy. Common staff and support services, facilities, or personnel skills may be employed. Modular product design and interchangeable components may offer a number of synergistic effects. Organizational capabilities may also enable improved balancing to be achieved internally to compensate for the varying demands between operations. Operational experience and capabilities in one manufacturing area may frequently be the catalyst and provide the know-how for introducing, improving, or expanding some other manufacturing activities. Although multiple organizational capabilities can commonly be mutually reinforcing, caution must be exercised to avoid a conglomeration of activities that might lead to the opposite effect. The development and acquisition, and pruning, of organizational capabilities are to be directed toward the establishment of a more virile, agile, and effective enterprise rather than primarily toward the enlargement of the organization. Organizational capabilities are to be nurtured that promise the fulfillment of total manufacturing objectives with maximum efficiency and effectiveness.

Finally, management capabilities can present a most powerful form of manufacturing synergy. Many manufacturing operations have been acquired largely for the management capabilities of the enterprise. Although the strategic capabilities of management are of paramount importance, numerous other kinds of management competence warrant consideration. Production management—planning, operations, and control—is an area where synergy can be a crucially competitive factor. Responsive financial control is also an area where management capabilities can play a synergistic role. Materials management and physical distribution constitute still another area where the impact of management competence can be multiplicative. The amplification potential of superior management is many times greater than that offered in the area of facilities and equipment or even in the areas of personnel skills and organizational capabilities. Management—the directing, adapting, and reorganizing intelligence of the manufacturing organism—is the skill and resource with the most challenging capability for manufacturing synergy.

The Gillette Company, while keeping the strict autonomy of its subsidiaries and divisions, has explored the synergistic opportunities offered by integrating its aerosol operations. Many of the toiletries produced by its subsidiary, Gillette Safety Razor Company, in Boston, and the hair-care products produced by its subsidiary, The

Toni Company, in St. Paul, employ almost identical aerosol technology and facilities. Among the strategic proposals evaluated have been the alternatives of integrating all aerosol operations for both subsidiaries at one location, or of fabricating all aerosol products in two or more consolidated facilities centered in the market areas for which the products are destined. The purported synergistic advantages of this strategic proposal are the more efficient utilization of specialized facilities and technology and the reduction of the physical distribution costs for products bearing high freight charges. An important negative consideration is the potential erosion of the operational authority and control of these autonomous subsidiaries. Although this proposal has not been accepted, adoption of the proposed realignment of these manufacturing activities may precipitate other important changes in the total strategy, orientation, and operations of the corporation.

The home furnishings industry has witnessed a variety of synergistic combinations. Noting the fragmentation and lethargic behavior of the furniture segment of this extensive industry, several outside manufacturers have acquired substantial positions within the furniture industry. Since 1964, Magnavox Company, which formerly possessed facilities for manufacturing cabinets for its consumer electronics equipment, has acquired Kent-Coffey Manufacturing Company (bedroom and occasional furniture) and Blowing Rock Chair Company (veneered traditional and contemporary dining room furniture). Within a two-year period, these furniture operations aggregated about 8 percent of total sales volume and yielded an attractive profit contribution—greater than the earnings on Magnavox's government business, although not yet comparable to its consumer electronics business. A similar strategy has been pursued by Mohasco Industries, Inc., producers of the Mohawk and Alexander Smith carpet lines. Acquisition of Firth Carpet Company made it the nation's largest carpet manufacturer. Since 1964, Mohasco has acquired Futorian Manufacturing Company, Super Sagless Spring Corporation, Barcalo Manufacturing Company, Chromcraft Company, and Basic-Witz Furniture Industries and now derives 30 percent of its sales volume from these furniture operations. Although early earnings from these acquisitions have been somewhat lower than the average earnings contributed by its carpet operations—to some extent owing to nonrecurring factors—

Mohasco predicts that the furniture operations will be contributing more than their proportionate share of earnings based upon volume within the near future. Burlington Industries, Inc., Welbilt Corporation, and Congoleum-Nairn, Inc., are other prominent manufacturers in the home furnishings industry that have recently established furniture manufacturing operations via acquisition. By selectively broadening its position in the home furnishings industry, each of these enterprises seeks in varying ways the manufacturing advantages of sales, resource, operations, or management synergy.

Thus animation can be infused into a manufacturing activity in many ways. The level of vitality is usually determined by both the number of ways and the intensities with which organizational animation is displayed. The purposeful pursuit of constructive change in the product-market mix as well as in product and production technology is one of the ways in which animation may be displayed; the intelligence to anticipate and exploit basic change in the socio-economic environment is another way in which animation may be displayed by the manufacturing organism.

Animation is characteristic of the manufacturing management that possesses the habit of thinking and planning strategically, that habitually perceives and pursues new product ideas, that habitually seeks and creates new technological opportunities, and that habitually develops and acquires new manufacturing capabilities. The directing intelligence of the manufacturing organism is concerned not only, or even primarily, with "doing today's jobs better" but also with defining the kinds of jobs that are going to be done tomorrow—five, ten, or more years from now. Most importantly, animation demands that the manufacturing organism exhibit one or several kinds of synergy—the organic phenomenon that amplifies the organization's inorganic component-inputs. Synergy can be achieved in sales, the utilization of resources, operations, and management; it may be most pronounced in ongoing operations or in the launching and start-up of new activities.

CONFLICTS

The demand for organizational animation is often in conflict with other desirable objectives. Animation assigns a high priority to progress, movement, flexibility, adaptability, and continuing re-organization. These attributes may be desirable, yet they can pre-clude the attainment of another essential organizational objective—equilibrium. Although the science of mechanics is concerned with both static and dynamic equilibrium, even dynamic equilibrium must be perceived in a fixed frame of reference. Analogously, an animated—or kinetic—strategy of manufacturing must be per-ceived in some fixed frame of reference. Periodically, this frame of reference may be modified and redefined, but any shifts must be undertaken consciously and explicitly.

In terms of day-to-day operations, equilibrium must be main-tained, and many things must be fixed or frozen for some anticipated period of time; this applies, for example, to product design, plant configuration, and sources of critical supply. The decision to im-prove upon a design may often be the responsibility of a configura-tion management group rather than engineering; after acceptance testing indicates that a system design satisfies all management speci-fications and performance criteria, and the design is frozen, this group—cognizant of the real costs of retrofit and system documen-tation changes—analyzes the total economy of any proposed im-provement and determines whether a configuration change is warranted. Disintegration rather than animation is displayed if the organism's actions and responses to external stimuli are allowed to become frenetic or ataxic. Facing this conflict, those concerned with the manufacturing strategy must determine with foresight and decisiveness what things *must* be fixed or frozen and then evaluate how significantly *these* things affect the organization's ability to exploit or adapt to varying eventualities and external situations.

One other type of conflict can arise in response to change. It has become a cliché to observe that manufacturing management must welcome, encourage, and seek change. However, maximum manufacturing profits are usually secured through highly mecha-nized or automated, repetitive, large-volume, long-term operations—activities where frequent changes can seldom be introduced easily or inexpensively. These operations, on the other hand, face the dilemma of producing commodities that eventually lead to narrow-ing profit margins rather than of producing diffierentiable products that frequently offer attractive profit margins but more limited scales of operations. Although manufacturing strategy is to foster and to stimulate change, uncontrolled change can engender insta-bility. By forecasting and even forcing change, a strategy of manu-facturing can anticipate and plan organizational mutations in a way that can avoid scarring effects to the organism.

Animation infuses into the manufacturing organism the attributes of life—the vitality and resiliency to promote growth and change. It introduces the synergy to foster internally adaptation, reorganiza-tion, and reproduction. Animation, the agency of organic intelli-gence, provides the manufacturing organism with the directing force to achieve strategic evolution, to create an organization capa-ble of competing in tomorrow's environment with maximum effectiveness.

VII

Automation

The circumstances of the world are so variable, that an irrevocable purpose or opinion is almost synonymous with a foolish one.
—William Henry Seward

Beautiful forms and compositions are not made by chance, nor can they ever, in any material, be made at small expense. A composition for cheapness and not excellence of workmanship is the most frequent and certain cause of the rapid decay and entire destruction of arts and manufactures.
—Josiah Wedgwood

W HILE *automation* is now a common and often-repeated word in our everyday vocabulary, it connotes many different things and concepts to different people. In one sense, automation implies replacing human operatives and artisans with automatic machines; in another, it implies continuous processing or on-line production; again, it implies rather elaborate controls and interconnections between individual operations, sometimes computer-directed, often incorporating feedback devices and closed-loop control circuits; and in still another sense, it implies an operation that is simply more mechanized than its predecessor. In each of these senses, automation is commonly used as a superlative to provide management and engineering ego-satisfactions or fodder for an ebullient public relations program. The adjectival expressions "the most automated" or "highly automated" are rather generally presumed to mean a manufacturing operation demonstrably better than either its predecessor or other alternatives.

Without digressing into the origins and history of the word *automation*, it is desirable to agree upon a definition. Essentially, automation in current parlance refers either to a whole or to selected aspects of a manufacturing activity where machines or devices initiate, perform, control, or monitor a number of operations—usually an appreciably larger number of operations—that formerly employed more manual techniques of implementation or control. Although this definition may appear to be circular, automation refers to operations that are notably more automatic than those previously prevalent in an industry, an organization, or other sphere, that display an enhanced level of automaticity in comparison with the common experience within a certain industrial situation. Automation results from the conscious, deliberate, and accelerating search for both improved and wholly new *labor-reducing* machines, processes, and material handling, workfeeding or transfer equipment. More automatic operations are usually based upon more extensive interconnections and interdependencies between manufacturing activities.

Although automation frequently suggests and does occasionally refer to a manufacturing activity exhibiting a new order of mechanization and automatic control, in practice it generally describes an operation that is simply more mechanized, more automatic, or, in many instances, more labor-reducing than some former standard. Extending the span of mechanization and automaticity—that is, automation—presupposes enhanced component reliability and responsive nonhuman control systems. Advanced self-correcting control mechanisms first incorporate a director with a predetermined program of action and ultimately embody a director responding to a variable in the environment; today, even heuristic control techniques are within the realm of technological—although seldom economic—feasibility.

However, despite the laudable advances that are continuing to be realized in extending the levels and applications of mechanization and automaticity as well as the enthusiasm of both the mass communications media and our more visionary engineers, automation has not wrought and cannot realistically be expected to achieve the socio-economic revolution so tediously predicted by both its most fanatical proponents and its most hysterical opponents. When we recognize that the aggregate productivity of manufacturing labor during the past decade or even the past two decades has not accelerated at a rate dramatically different from the average rate observed during the past century—approximately 0.2 percent per decade—it is difficult to claim that automation is anything more than the vigorous continuation of the process of mechanization, automatic control, and replacement of manual by electromechanical operations that has been occurring since the advent of the Industrial Revolution. (Although "electromechanical" accurately describes the nature of almost all automated systems and equipments developed to date, important achievements are being scored through new technologies such as pneumatic, hydraulic, and fluidic control that may be expected increasingly to characterize automated installations within the near future.)

Automation may not be a revolutionary phenomenon, but it is unquestionably an important vector of socio-economic evolution. It is the physical manifestation of the continually changing relationship between the economic factors of production—labor, land, capital, and technology—as the first two factors become comparatively more scarce when matched against our rising expectations and the latter two become more plentiful. Perceived in the simplest terms, the ever increasing demand for labor and land, owing to their relative scarcity, has been raising the cost of these factors in comparison with capital and technology which are becoming common, more abundant, and consequently less costly. The interaction of many other societal influences supports and augments this general long-range trend. Thus, while automation may not be a cataclysmic phenomenon, it is one of several primary socio-economic developments of the latter half of the 20th century—one of the major forces continually influencing the direction, character, meaning, and goals of our industrial society.

Advantages

Among the promises of automation, cost reduction is one of the obvious and most common advantages. The simplest case is that in which the total economic cost of performing an operation or a cluster of operations more mechanically or automatically is substantially less than the incremental cost of human operatives to perform these activities. However, automation can secure many other types of cost reductions.

It has been noted that the long-range inflationary bias in our total economy commends increasing the ratio of committed (fixed) costs to product (variable) costs to render manufacturing activities less sensitive to increases in these product (variable) costs, especially direct labor characterized by its unrelenting wage increases. This consideration suggests that, even though an economic evaluation of a contemplated automation program reveals that little more than the organization's minimum rate of return may be met under present conditions, the program could still be desirable as a way of fixing most of the cost inputs of the activity and of providing greater immunity against the virtually certain increases in direct labor costs in the future. In the face of the realities of capital rationing, alternative automation programs or other investment opportunities offering substantially higher rates of return should certainly be undertaken prior to considering a borderline case scarcely meeting the organization's minimum rate of return.

The elimination or substantial curtailment of premium wages for overtime work is another way in which an automated manufacturing activity—usually through higher operating rates—can achieve attractive overall cost reductions. This is an outstanding consideration in several of the more socialized Western European economies where certain types of overtime work are severely penalized, if not totally prohibited, thereby justifying levels of automation frequently more advanced than their industry counterparts in the United States. Automated operations can usually realize cost reductions through lowering setup times, changeover times, testing and inspection times, scrap and wastage, and the incidence of human error. The realistic identification and evaluation of all sources of potential cost reduction customarily constitute the first and one of the most important steps in the analysis of a contemplated program of automation.

A closely related, but distinct, area of exploration is the changing composition of labor and supervisory skills that has resulted from raising the level of mechanization and automatic control. Generalizations are always subject to qualifications and exceptions; nevertheless, numerous investigations indicate that automated operations usually demand enhanced engineering and maintenance skills, whereas the skill content of line operatives is often decreased. Aside from the important and fascinating questions surrounding the psychological effects of, and union reactions to, the changing composition of skills, this phenomenon introduces critical questions affecting the formulation of a strategy of manufacturing. The internal development and external recruitment of engineering, supervisory, and maintenance personnel with the requisite potential skills is equally—often more—imperative than the design of the automated facilities. The start-up and debugging problems accompanying a new facility, as well as the failure of many ongoing operations to sustain design capacity, can frequently be attributed to human rather than to hardware deficiencies. The proper selection, training, motivation, and direction of engineering, supervisory, and maintenance personnel are paramount if the proper performance of an automated facility is to be achieved; this consideration warrants even greater attention when an operation must be located in an area where it is difficult to attract and retain individuals with these critical skills.

Although an automated operation is often attended by a marked increase in both the numbers and skills of "indirect" and support personnel, the numbers and skill levels of line operatives are frequently diminished. Today and at least within the meaningful future, the fully automated plant operated by a computer and a handful of engineers to correct any possible, but unlikely, equipment malfunctions is still more an aspiration than an actuality. The most advanced oil refineries still employ thousands of men, while at the most recently designed plants in the automotive industry—the industry that gave birth to the word *automation* and has long been noted for a comparatively high level of mechanization and automatic control—many thousands of men can be seen entering and leaving at every change of shift. Therefore, although automation may not be expected to eliminate the line operative, certain changes can be observed and a continuation of these trends can be forecast:

- As it has for more than a century, manufacturing technology will continue to introduce new types of labor-reducing machines and devices as the combination of the increasing cost of labor with these technological achievements justify such capital investments. This trend will continue to cause a steady, but rarely dramatic, reduction in the numbers of on-line operatives for a specific operation.

· Manufacturing technology can be expected to score more fundamental successes in reducing the skill content of production jobs, thereby reducing the requisite operative skills (and relative compensation) and, most significantly, qualifying many more applicants—especially women and unskilled or semiskilled men—for production jobs that currently demand skilled operatives.

· As an automated activity is developed to a level where it must be manned by a programmed force, and output can be varied primarily by the hours or shifts of operation rather than by the numbers of direct labor employed, line operatives become less a variable cost and more a programmed or fixed cost of operation.

Thus each of these three changes in the content and nature of the line operatives' jobs exerts a major influence upon the formulation of a strategy of manufacturing.

Frequently, an automated activity can offer the important advantage of lead-time reduction when model changes or new product specifications are encountered. Reduced lead time can be realized by programming in various ways many of the task directions that formerly required manual planning techniques or lengthy operative training sessions. For example: Once the sizable job of preparing a program for each anticipated task has been completed, numerically controlled equipment can shift from one task to any one of hundreds or thousands of other tasks swiftly and simply just by indexing to the appropriate tape director. Automated production equipment generally incorporates increasingly extensive, but basically quite simple, automatic electromechanical control and adjustment devices that permit product specifications and characteristics to be modified with a minimum of down time. These equipment capabilities enable production changes to be made quickly and economically, averting many sources of human error with their attendant high scrap rates and diminishing, if not eliminating, the importance of learning times and the significance of learning curves. This advantage of an automated facility, however, is limited to those product changes that can be anticipated and programmed into the system; if new or desired product specifications should exceed the facility's design criteria, equipment modifications to accommodate these changes—if possible—may be exceedingly costly and time consuming.

In many instances, the impetus and rationale to automate an activity may be the inability of any alternative facility to satisfy capacity criteria. Once a certain scale of operations is attained, a plant embodying a high level of mechanization and automatic control may be the only *physically* feasible alternative, even though total unit costs may not be appreciably lower than those exhibited by a smaller less-automated plant. The logistics of assembling, handling, and transforming large volumes of materials and products often exceeds the capabilities of anything other than a highly mechanized operation. An automated facility can often multiply its output with only a modest increase in total cost by running two or three shifts per day; in numerous cases, this consideration justifies substantial increases in the level of mechanization and automatic control. Invariably, increasing output by increasing the number of operatives introduces diseconomies and operational inductance. A judicious program of automation can provide the facilities needed to achieve large-volume output without relying upon a workforce of unwieldy proportions.

Frequently, enhanced mechanization and automatic control are the only means of securing quality improvement and product uniformity. These criteria can be satisfied not only through automated production equipment but also through the introduction of more sensitive and reliable in-line testing and inspection equipment. By eliminating operative variability and potential sources of human error, an automated manufacturing activity can maintain higher standards of product quality and reliability, which frequently lead to new market opportunities, more attractive price schedules, and the elimination of excessive scrap and wastage; and it often permits a downgrading of input specifications yielding consequential economies. Many rigid product specifications can be satisfied only through the use of automated manufacturing facilities; in other instances, improved quality standards resulting in enhanced product reliability may engender greater customer satisfaction, confidence, and loyalty. The combination of quality improvement and product uniformity can be an important objective of a strategy of manufacturing and a crucial consideration in embarking upon a program of automation.

One of the most challenging developments in the electronics industry is large-scale integration—the construction of complete communications or computer subsystems embodying thousands of transistors, resistors, capacitors, and diodes on a single wafer of silicon or other semiconductive material. This technology offers enhanced reliability, faster operating speeds, and potentially lower costs as well as an absence of complexity and specialization; however, only in a high-volume automated facility is it feasible to produce large-scale integrated circuits. The magnitude, cost, and complex electromechanical characteristics of the necessary automated facilities demand that the manufacturer of components and subsystems employing large-scale integration secure substantial sales volume and that the industry achieve a degree of standardization not formerly acceptable.

In view of the market expansion that can be anticipated to result from markedly reduced component costs, the manufacturing strategy implications that accompany this emerging technology are momentous and can be expected to evoke significant realignments within the industry. The fundamental question arises from the roles to be performed by the traditional components manufacturers, such as General Instrument Corporation, versus the systems manufacturers, such as International Business Machines Corporation, and the components and systems manufacturers, such as General Electric Company and Texas Instruments Incorporated. (It is of special interest to note that the latter two groups presently represent major customers of the former.) Thus a large-scale integrated circuit manufacturing capability requires not only the resources and technological skills to establish automated production facilities possessing a high level of sophistication but also the management foresight and conviction to seek and occupy positions of manufacturing/marketing superiority in the most promising and competitive technology germinating in the electronics industry.

DISADVANTAGES

An advantage is seldom unalloyed. In many cases—probably in most cases, if all industry is included—the disadvantages of automation obviate its promise. These disadvantages usually fall into one of two categories:

- The almost definitional conflict of excessively limited flexibility or, as previously suggested, what can be described as inadequate physical liquidity.
- The requirement for fairly long-term investments of a magnitude that may conflict with the organization's capital budgeting policies or capabilities.

A thoughtful investigation of these considerations will often lead to the disapproval or substantial revision of a contemplated plan of automation that is otherwise interesting and ambitious.

Many kinds of flexibility limitations may be encountered. Inasmuch as most forms of mechanization and automatic control tend to limit a facility to performing exclusively those operations that can be anticipated, defined quantitatively, and programmed into the system, the breadth of product line and variations in product specifications can be altered easily only within these predetermined constraints. This characteristic often makes exceeding these predetermined bounds prohibitively costly, if not physically impossible. Consequently, this type of limitation on flexibility can present manufacturing management in the future with an awkward dilemma: Whether it is best to forgo attractive and even essential product development opportunities because of the major costs (and "book losses") associated with redesigning and modifying existing facilities to accommodate new product specifications or to abandon existing facilities prematurely and make the substantial investment required to establish a modified or expanded plant embodying the capabilities to satisfy new product specifications. Even the latter alternative is likely to incorporate flexibility limitations that may prove to be uncomfortably restricting and embarrassing within the near future.

Although it is technically possible to design automated facilities that demonstrate a high degree of flexibility to accommodate a very broad range of product specifications, economic evaluations usually direct that potential flexibility remain within fairly narrow limits. Recognizing the rapid rate of obsolescence that characterizes these facilities owing to their inflexibility, manufacturing management frequently attempts to compensate for this factor by using comparatively short expected service lives in the evaluation of contemplated automation programs or even by assigning considerable weight to such a crude index as payout period. The latter technique can be criticized by operations analysts, but it is useful to note that payout period—which can be defined as a measure of liquidity rather than rate of return or investment profitability—is being employed by management with considerable insight to measure "physical" as well as financial liquidity, or flexibility, the factor exerting a primary influence on the possible success of a contemplated program of automation.

Customarily, 80 or 90 percent of the component equipment in the most automated facility is standard equipment that has been available for years, with only minor mechanical or control modifications to make it compatible with its feed and take-away units. However, this standard equipment loses most of its independent flexibility by being embodied in a larger assemblage, where it can only operate upon the narrowly defined work that can be fed to it and removed to the next operation. In the traditional machine shop, a turret lathe can machine hydraulic cylinders and rotors for electric motors with equal ease; the turret lathe components in an automated truck-axle plant can only produce truck axles within a limited range of specifications. If the specifications for truck axles must be revised beyond the capabilities of the total equipment assemblage, or the production of truck axles is to be transferred to another plant, the automated facility—including the turret lathe components —has very little utility or flexibility to accept other types of work.

The Ford Motor Company's engine plant in Cleveland has become a classic case study in automation. This example appears to have special relevance, since it is commonly acknowledged that the word *automation* was coined by Mr. D. S. Harder, then vice president of manufacturing for Ford, at a facilities planning conference in 1946 to describe automatic material handling and work-feeding. Between 1949 and 1951, Ford designed and built a new engine plant in Cleveland where a comprehensive effort was made to achieve a notably higher level of automation than had been realized in any similar facility. Although this achievement became world-famous, it should be noted that most of the component equipment was comparatively standard, that many operations were still performed manually, that only two models of a single product were produced, and that Ford's management was never unanimous in claiming that this plant was an outstandingly successful undertaking.

However, it ran for eight years without major modifications until, in 1959–1960, Ford redesigned its engines, deemed the existing facilities to be too inflexible, and rebuilt the engine plant. In the annals of automation, this installation exhibited remarkable longevity and can now be considered to have been a successful venture by almost any standard; nevertheless, its demise was attributed to inflexibility—its inability to accept the increasing variations and more frequent design changes in engine characteristics and sizes.

The sensitivity of an automated facility to variations in raw materials or other inputs represents another way in which flexibility may be limited. Frequently, it is imperative to establish more rigid purchasing specifications to avoid input irregularities that may result in equipment malfunctions or stoppages. These requirements can be accompanied not only by some increase in input cost—a factor to be acknowledged in an economic evaluation—but also by a constriction of the sources of supply due to the inability of certain suppliers to comply with the more rigid specifications. In these cases, the flexibility of the facility is limited when it is incapable of accepting alternative inputs or drawing upon alternative sources of supply.

Production scheduling is another area of operations where automation may exhibit inflexibility. The high cost of down time and change-over time necessitates the careful planning and scheduling of production—often for a period extending several days or even weeks into the future—to assure the maximum utilization of equipment. Although a number of automated activities are remarkable in being able to respond economically to schedule changes on very short notice, it is observed more generally that production schedules cannot be altered on short notice and, in certain instances, cannot be modified too drastically from the anticipated schedules upon which the design of the installation was based. Obviously, these constraints may be intolerable when matched against the marketing strategy of the organization.

An automated plant is invariably designed to operate at a specific rate of output—50 units per minute or 80 tons per hour. Although the equipment may be capable of running at a slower rate, this is usually unacceptably inefficient because personnel requirements or crew size are fixed by whether or not the equipment is running rather than by the rate at which it is running. Therefore, fluctuations in output demand can only be met by varying the hours or shifts of operation for the total plant, and little reduction in total cost will be realized if most input costs, including labor, are essentially committed or programmed rather than variable. The nature of many automated operations—for example, certain petrochemical processes —demands that they be run at a steady rate without interruption or shutdown. In these cases, the facility is usually designed to satisfy the maximum anticipated demand (or volume the organization desires to meet); short-term reductions in volume are accommodated simply by producing at standard output to inventory, and longer-term reductions in volume require a major plant shutdown for an extended period of time. Thus an automated activity may not exhibit sufficient flexibility to respond easily or economically to important changes in volume and output demand.

The other possible disadvantage of an automated operation can be the substantial capital investment requirement in comparison with less automated alternatives. It is presumed that any contemplated program of automation will be subject to a thorough economic analysis and will receive no further consideration unless it compares favorably with less automated alternatives. However, even an otherwise attractive program may be discarded for one of two reasons:

- The magnitude of the required capital investment may exceed the present capabilities of the organization or limits established through a supposedly prudent policy of capital budgeting.
- The rapid or uncertain rate of obsolescence, or the purported risks associated with establishing an automated activity embodying many advanced features, may lead to revised evaluations based upon an unusually short service life; or circumstances may simply lead to a management decision to avoid a comparatively large capital investment which, even though forecast to yield an attractive return, displays so many troubling uncertainties.

These considerations should not be of consequence for a large soundly financed organization, but the magnitude of the requisite capital investment can be a deterrent to the small organization embarking upon a program of automation.

The investment in software required for an automated operation is often of substantial proportions and may rival the investment required to procure and install the basic hardware. Industrial

137

management's increasing understanding and use of the computer may lead to an enhanced awareness of the importance and substantial cost of appropriate software; many computer installations require a $500,000 to $1 million investment in programming and related software, such as compilers, prewritten programs, utility programs, and operating systems. It is not uncommon for software to represent 20 to 40 percent of the cost of an automated manufacturing system. This software can include production scheduling and control systems, in-process material management data, operating instructions, training manuals, repair and maintenance manuals, and —for computer-directed operations—complex and costly command systems. In developing and introducing its System/360, IBM invested almost as much in programming systems support as in the total development of hardware. The magnitude of this effort was not fully anticipated and has been estimated to exceed $200 million. In addition to the direct costs associated with this phase of the System/360 project, the dimensions of the effort have resulted in delays in the development of the advanced programming systems that are required to enable the large-scale computers and time-sharing systems to achieve their full design capabilities.

CHARACTERISTICS

An automated facility usually exhibits a number of significant attributes when compared with alternative manufacturing facilities. It has been observed that an automated activity is characterized by a high degree of interdependency—both internally and externally. Operationally, each machine may be interconnected and synchronized with every other machine, and each machine's proper performance is dependent primarily upon every other machine performing at rated capacity. With few ways, if any, of bypassing or circumventing a malfunctioning component, a high order of component reliability becomes mandatory. The failure or even below-standard performance of any component within the assemblage can result in a major disruption to the total operation. Interdependency demands that raw and in-process materials meeting rigid specifications be delivered to the right point in the right quantities at the right time; often, the configuration and space limitations of automated equipment preclude maintaining in-process inventories at intermediate work stations to satisfy production requirements for more than a few minutes or, at best, a few hours. In recognition of its sensitivity to any malfunction, disruption, or shutdown, the interdependency of an automated facility assigns particular importance and urgency to the engineering design of the plant, the competence of the maintenance force and thoroughness of preventive maintenance programs, the authority of production planning and control, and the training of both the line operatives and especially supervisors. Interdependency may also be demonstrated through the operation's relations with external material suppliers, parts and component suppliers, and service organizations, as well as with almost all of the enterprise's other functional activities.

The high cost of changes is another characteristic of automation that can be displayed in several ways. Even during the period of design and installation, project changes in design criteria or characteristics frequently result in delays and substantial added costs. Once the facility is operational, modifications beyond those anticipated by the design criteria may be prohibitively expensive, not only because of the nature of changes in hardware but also because of the prolonged down time often required to accomplish these changes. The high cost of changes underscores the importance of the initial design concept in forecasting technological and product changes and in establishing adequate design criteria for the facility. Although the operational details of the design of an automated facility can seldom be viewed as a secondary consideration, a preoccupation with these engineering mechanics should never be allowed to distort or dilute the dominance of a hypermetropic design concept. An ill-conceived program of automation can lead either to costly facilities changes within the near future or—often the more expensive alternative—to renouncing otherwise attractive or even essential product changes and additions owing to the high cost of modifying an only partially amortized facility.

Product redesign is often a prerequisite of automation. This characteristic is attributed to the need to transport, manipulate, and transform the product—usually by electromechanical means—through an extended series of operations. Product redesign frequently simplifies or expedites the design of more extensive machines, mechanical devices, and automatic control systems to perform various operations in the manufacture of the product. In many cases, this requirement results in little change in the outward appearance or performance of the product; not uncommonly, substantial product improvements may ensue. In other cases, however, product redesign can result in substantial changes in the outward appearance or performance of the product and may invite strong consumer reactions.

Although consumer reactions may be either positive or negative, a carefully planned program of consumer education may be able to transform a potentially negative reaction into a positive acceptance or demand for the redesigned product, thereby securing another competitive advantage through automation. When introducing continuous-mix bread—a major step toward further automation in a large-scale bakery—this tactic has been employed with marked success by several baking companies in a variety of market areas by emphasizing to the consumer the attractive features of the new product in contrast to the purported deficiencies in conventional bread. Because preference in bread taste and appearance vary geographically, this tactic has not been effective universally, and continuous-mix bread still lacks broad consumer acceptance in certain market areas in northeastern United States and in eastern Canada. The consequences of product redesign can be pervasive and occasionally disastrous. A program of automation must carefully evaluate the product characteristics affected by redesign and anticipate the ways in which any negative consumer reactions can be dispelled.

Increasing automation tends to increase committed and programmed (fixed) costs in relationship to product (variable) costs, to alter the composition of operating costs, and to raise the breakeven point for the affected activity. Although the minimum level of operations to break even is usually raised substantially, an automated plant exhibits greater leverage than less automated alternatives; this characteristic can be attractive if a level of operations substantially above the breakeven point can be forecast with confidence. It has been noted (1) that an automated facility is expected to result in substantially lower total cost per unit of output at the forecast levels of operation and (2) that the operation becomes less vulnerable to anticipated increases in variable costs, especially labor, resulting from the long-range inflationary bias in the total economy produced by increasing the ratio of "fixed" costs to "variable" costs.

Although these expected advantages of automation warrant thoughtful investigation, recognition must be given to the fact that a higher breakeven point introduces another type of inflexibility. An automated facility that cannot be operated at rated capacity, or at least above its breakeven point, can rapidly generate substantial losses; whereas income contribution may escalate swiftly under favorable conditions, the leverage of automation can multiply losses with comparable rapidity if unfavorable conditions should be encountered. Thus thorough market analysis and forecasting assume greater urgency when automation is an important component of manufacturing strategy.

STRATEGIC PLANNING CONSIDERATIONS

A program of automation demands that production requirements be planned with precision. Product characteristics, sales volumes, and operating schedules as well as the limits within which each of these factors may be expected to fluctuate must be defined specifically in the design criteria; even the service life of the production system must be stated unequivocally during the planning and design stage. An automated production system may not be easily expanded in the traditional ways—"adding 18 more machines" or "adding another 100,000 square feet to the plant"—and output characteristics may not be modified simply by rebuilding or replacing component equipment. Rather, facility expansions and modifications exceeding those anticipated and planned for in the design criteria frequently require nothing less than rebuilding of the total installation. This consideration again emphasizes the crucial role of manufacturing strategy and its translation into the design concept for an activity that is to embody a high level of automation. Formerly answers to many questions could be deferred until after an operation was on stream, but an automated operation demands that almost all questions surrounding both near-term and long-range production requirements be answered, specifically and quantitatively, during the design stage; in many cases, appreciable research and analysis must precede the answers to these design questions. It should be observed that efforts to define production requirements with precision are commonly in conflict with a fundamental industry trend toward more frequent product changes, greater variation in product specifications and customer-designated configurations, accelerating technological evolution, and unpredictable competition from nontraditional sources.

In view of the relative inflexibility of automated facilities, the possible or likely reactions of competitors to automation warrant careful investigation. Competitive reactions may be triggered either by general industry and technological developments, or by a significant installation by one manufacturer. After examining the developments or installation arousing interest, these reactions may take the form of making little change in existing operations—either because the developments or installation appear to present no competitive challenge or because they cannot be utilized by the manufacturing competitor—or of attempting to duplicate and possibly surpass the most advanced achievements to date, or of mounting a concentrated counterattack at those points where an automated activity is most vulnerable.

The strategy of manufacturing must anticipate each of these competitive reactions to a program of automation and incorporate any necessary countermeasures. The lack of any strong response often indicates that the automation program is perceived by competitors as being ill-advised, hence posing no competitive threat or offering them some competitive advantage. An effort to duplicate or surpass an advanced installation frequently results in the automating pioneer receiving the industry plaudits while possessing a prematurely obsolete facility. And competitors' discovery and counterattack at those points where an automated activity is revealed to be especially vulnerable may be either a mere nuisance or the undoing of an inauspicious undertaking. Invariably, one of these responses must be encountered; a sound program of automation will demonstrate sufficient defensive strengths to repel any dangerous incursions by competitors.

A program of automation must always recognize the possibility of the radical or unanticipated technological development that would swiftly render today's advanced installation obsolete. Although it is still a very uncertain discipline, technological forecasting is now beginning to employ the tools of rational analysis and industrial intelligence instead of the former exclusive reliance upon clairvoyance. To the alert and inquisitive industrial manager, technological breakthroughs are seldom unpredictable; in the wake of laboratory or pilot plant success, months or even years still usually must elapse before the more revolutionary technological breakthroughs can be developed into commercially reliable equipment. When the fact is accepted that the expected service lives of automated installations in the more technologically volatile industries range from two to five years, a conscientious effort to forecast significant technological developments can usually result in making appropriate provisions to accommodate any important developments anticipated and to preclude the danger as well as the embarrassment of subsequent surprise.

Technological forecasting will influence the timing of a program of automation. Timing takes into account both when an automated manufacturing system should be introduced and when each step of an automation program should be executed. Although tradition suggests that an operation be automated whenever it is economically justified, the nature of today's more extensive, sensitive, and interdependent manufacturing systems makes the consideration of timing increasingly more complex. In one case, a program of automation may be readily justified economically; however, the imminence of an important technological development may indicate that the program be deferred for a period of time, since this forecast development is expected to result in the industry adopting manufacturing systems of a new configuration with radically improved performance characteristics. In another case, a conventional economic analysis may fail to justify a contemplated program of automation; however, the program may still be attractive and should be undertaken in view of forecast requirements within the measurable future that can be satisfied only with an automated manufacturing facility. This would involve a major increase in volume demand; frequent and numerous changes in product configuration within the design capabilities of the proposed facility; enhanced product quality, reliability, or uniformity standards; or the immediate need to establish a new plant with a long anticipated service life, which would be prohibitively expensive to replace or rebuild within the near future. Again, technological forecasting can provide invaluable industry intelligence and insight with which to resolve the question of strategic timing.

143

The type of product line is another consideration that affects the role of automation in a manufacturing strategy. The opportunities for automation may be restricted for an operation where critical aspects of raw materials are unstable or widely variable, where finished products must exhibit multiformity, or where the market will not accept a product with a machinemade appearance. The characteristics of today's product line are to be investigated, but special attention must be devoted to the product-line characteristics of the future; in most instances, tomorrow's product line will be more variform, more fractionated, and may even be composed of different raw materials or other inputs. At the earliest possible time, the analysis, planning, and design of an automated installation must be founded upon an intimate and objective knowledge of the present product line plus an imaginative comprehension of the character and composition of tomorrow's product line. The nature of the product line, established through a rigorous definition of product criteria and objectives, will exert a primary influence upon the degree and extent of mechanization and automatic control to be incorporated into a manufacturing activity.

Finally, product stability determines the potential scope of automation. Petroleum, aluminum, flour, paper, industrial chemicals, and similar commodities have employed highly automated manufacturing processes for many years. Even though these commodity industries continue to develop improved manufacturing facilities, it is rash to claim that the achievements in automation during the past decade (or those forecast for the next decade) are any more revolutionary than those that have occurred during each decade since 1900. At the opposite end of the spectrum, innumerable products have such a short or uncertain market life that an extensively automated manufacturing system cannot be economically feasible. Included in this category are high-fashion merchandise, products subject to rapid and continuing technological development and change, many kinds of products produced under military and aerospace contracts—often liable to cancellation—and even formerly stable products that must now compete in restructured and fragmented markets.

The most challenging situations, however, are usually found between the two extremes of product stability, where product life can be measured in terms of a few years rather than in months or decades without radical change and substantial volume in terms of units appears to be assured. The manufacture of automobiles, household appliances, television and air-conditioning equipment, carpets and apparel fabrics, and many convenience food products falls into this intermediate category. The investigation of a plant producing a commodity product seldom reveals any important operations where further automation might be introduced and would be technically feasible. Still, the knowledgeable evaluation of any plant in this intermediate category would identify many activities where further automation is technically, if not economically, feasible; the changeable nature of the product and uncertain market life are usually the deterrents to more extensively automated facilities. For example, the production of propane as an alternate fraction in the refining of aviation gasoline suggests few opportunities for further automation, while the manufacture of polypropylene packaging materials (using propylene resins derived primarily from propane) is an operation where the absence of prolonged product stability may preclude the installation of a production plant exhibiting a high order of automation.

Automation is commonly perceived as a physical attribute to be acquired in the form of a specific plant, equipment, or automatic control system; yet it is essentially an attitude and orientation of management—directing the conscious, deliberate, and accelerating search for both improved and wholly new labor-reducing ways of manufacturing things. The totally automated facility is still virtually unknown, and its realization cannot be expected within the immediate future. Consequently, a strategy of manufacturing is rarely concerned with effecting a revolution in current manufacturing techniques but rather with planning and organizing the resources to effect a step-by-step advance in the levels of mechanization and automatic control for those manufacturing activities where and when each step is warranted economically or strategically. A prudent program of automation is formulated by:

- Perceiving those operations where substantial reductions in labor or other gains are most needed, would be most attractive, and are technologically feasible.
- Evaluating quantitatively the economic and strategic costs and anticipated returns associated with each contemplated step.
- Planning the ways in which the requisite resources (men,

facilities, and money) are to be acquired and deployed to achieve each step on schedule with maximum effectiveness.

Enhanced levels of mechanization and automatic control are often exhibited in specific new facilities; yet automation is primarily a program of sequential goals and of improving standards to be incorporated into manufacturing systems and equipments in conformance with a thoughtfully conceived overall plan. Automation is never an objective in itself; it is an attribute of the physical tools with which an imaginative strategy of manufacturing is to be implemented.

VIII

Action

> *Thinking well is wise; planning well, wiser; doing well, wisest and best of all.*
> —Persian proverb

> *We should not only master questions, but also act upon them, and act definitely.*
> —Woodrow Wilson

FORMULATING A STRATEGY of manufacturing precedes the enactment of the strategy in importance as well as in time. Admittedly, a superior strategic plan that is not executed or is bungled in execution has little value. However, a soundly conceived and carefully planned strategy of manufacturing reduces implementation to the operational level—a level still fraught with important and almost numberless managerial problems but hopefully spared from making strategic decisions on the run. In many cases, an outstanding strategic plan can withstand defects in execution and still achieve its selected objectives effectively; on the other hand, an uninspired strategy of manufacturing or the absence of a plan will seriously erode the most vigorous efforts of operational management. The critical point of action is not the implementation of a plan but the thoughtful formulation and thorough exposition of a strategy of manufacturing. If senior management acts continually and deliberately in fulfilling its strategic planning obligations, both the authority and the responsibility to execute these carefully delineated manufacturing plans can be delegated to operational management with confidence.

The formulation and enactment of an imaginative strategy of manufacturing are demonstrated by The Carborundum Company, a venerable producer of industrial abrasives. Between 1962 and 1966, this organization's sales revenues moved from $150.5 million to $230.6 million, and industrial abrasives—while growing in absolute sales—dropped from more than 80 percent of total sales to approximately 60 to 65 percent of worldwide revenues. Recognizing that its primary manufacturing resource is its competence to produce inorganic refractory and ceramic materials of high purity capable of resisting elevated temperatures and mechanical wear, the company has pursued a strategy to multiply the effectiveness of these manufacturing assets.

Although ten acquisitions have been consummated during this period, one of the first strategic acts was to implement a pervasive program of corporate reorganization, cost reduction, and expanded capital investment. The industrial abrasives operations have been transformed from the production and sale of grinding wheels to the manufacture and marketing of abrasives systems encompassing all associated equipment. Carborundum's refractory capabilities have resulted in the development of a degausser—a proprietary device to segregate color on color television sets. High-purity refractory materials are also produced for electrical apparatus, such as heating devices and computers, as well as for special-purpose refractory brick. In 1966, Carborundum's expanding interests in ceramics led to the acquisition of W. T. Copeland & Sons, the British producer of Spode china since 1770. Its production of boron nitride and alumina silica fibers possessing exceptional insulation qualities offer attractive opportunities for substantial growth and new product applications, while its production of silicon carbide "whiskers," carbon graphite fibers, and silicon-carbide-coated graphite is establishing a prominent position in the exciting field of fiber composite materials. These actions are the manifestations of a manufacturing strategy that has been formulated with diligence and vision, and enunciated with precision by Carborundum's senior management.

Thus the crucial strategic act is the act of formulating a realistic strategy. The efficacy of this activity is centered upon such questions as who is to formulate manufacturing strategy, how this strategy is to be formulated, how operational management is to be involved in strategy formulation and to be apprised of strategic plans, and how strategy is to be enacted and controlled.

DIRECTION OF SENIOR MANAGEMENT

Essentially by definition, strategic planning is the province and a foremost responsibility of senior management. For most organizations, senior management is comprised primarily of the directors and secondarily of specific corporate officers—the chairman of the board, the chief executive officer, the president, and members of certain committees of the board of directors, such as an executive committee or strategic (long-range) planning committee. Although strategic planning activities may coalesce around one officer-director, it is the board of directors that is charged with the ultimate responsibility of strategy formulation. Without minimizing the concurrent importance of monitoring ongoing operations, the fact remains that strategic planning is the natural function as well as an active, continuing, and cardinal obligation of the board of directors. Corporate strategy embodies several functional components, such as financial strategy, marketing strategy, and manufacturing strategy. Although the relative importance and complexity of each of these functional strategies vary from industry to industry and organization to organization, the directors cannot abdicate the responsibility or avoid involvement in the formulation of each of the functional strategies. In the formulation of a strategy of manufacturing, however, the work of the directors can be supplemented and greatly expanded through the design and utilization of a responsive strategic information system.

STRATEGIC COMMUNICATIONS

Strategic communications differ fundamentally from operational communications. This is due to the type of information, the points at which it is generated, and the speed with which it must be transmitted. Operational planning and control can be based almost entirely upon numerical or quantitative information, most of which is generated at specific points within the organization and usually must be transmitted to management with the greatest possible speed; consequently, on-line computers permitting the design and utilization of real-time manufacturing planning and control systems fulfill an invaluable role in meeting the information and communication needs of operational management.

However, while every effort is to be made to quantify non-numerical factors, strategic planning and control are inevitably based upon both qualitative and quantitative information. This information is derived from sources within the organization as well as from important external sources, and a transmission time of days or even weeks or months generally satisfies all reasonable needs of senior management. Rather than employing on-line computers to generate real-time data, strategy formulation is based upon the evaluation of industry and functional trends, the appraisal of technological and market forecasts, and the systematic collection and organization of often disparate data through an extensive and sensitive network of both internal and external industrial intelligence. This type of strategic information rarely flows through the routine channels of operational management and, to avoid distortion and possible loss, should not be transmitted through these operational channels; on the contrary, strategic information should be transmitted through distinct and formally defined channels of strategic communication. These channels of strategic communication must accommodate many types of staff and operational reports plus—most importantly—a myriad of verbal contacts.

The design of a strategic information system is approached in much the same way as the design of any other management information system. First, it is imperative to recognize that in even the smallest or most informal organization some type of strategic information system is needed and probably exists; the rare recognition of this need leads to an appreciation of the improvements to be achieved through conscious system design. And, second, the design of the strategic information system is to be directed toward answering questions such as these: What type of strategic information is needed? Who needs it? Who is to collect it? From what sources is it to come? How urgently is it needed? In what form is this information to be transmitted and presented to senior management? The answers to these questions invariably will result in the design of a strategic information system of a totally different configuration than that assumed by the organization's operational information system. The design of each of these information systems will provide for interties at critical points where common information is needed.

A strategic information system will generally process four kinds of information:

- Industrial intelligence derived largely from external sources.
- Inputs from staff and consulting specialists.
- Inputs from operational management.
- Outputs including directives from senior management.

INDUSTRIAL INTELLIGENCE

The systematic collection and organization of industrial intelligence constitute an indispensable activity too often neglected in the formulation of a manufacturing strategy. Although industrial espionage and covert techniques of securing information are both repugnant and seldom of any critical importance, the orderly use of the many overt techniques of industrial intelligence can provide invaluable information in the areas of technological forecasting, market developments, and competitors' resources and observable strategies. In several of the largest industrial enterprises, formal staff groups performing G-2 functions (to borrow from military parlance) are to be encountered. Even though the planning needs of most organizations may not demand such specialists, it is essential that overt means of intelligence be exploited and that systematic procedures, channels of communications, and organizational arrangements be established to process and utilize industrial intelligence. It is instructive to note that the most startling and revolutionary industrial events almost never occur without adequate forewarning; in retrospect, the methodical employment of the overt techniques of industrial intelligence would have routinely predicted each of these so-called surprising and unexpected events.

Complementing and frequently also undertaking the industrial intelligence function, internal staff specialists and competent external consultants can provide essential support in collecting and organizing pertinent data, introducing for consideration alternative objectives, resources, and courses of action, evaluating significant trends and developments, and employing the more rigorous quantitative techniques of analyzing the anticipated characteristics and performance of contemplated strategies. In a small organization, this work may be undertaken by an operations analyst or executive assistant, or by the periodic engagement of a knowledgeable consultant; in a larger organization, a specialized staff continually engaged in the analysis and planning of manufacturing strategy may be appropriate. These staff and consulting services often achieve superior communication and coordination with other functional and staff efforts within the organization as well as with critical external activities; they can provide more comprehensive in-depth investigations than could be achieved by one or two directors or senior officers, and can frequently maintain more balanced objectivity than can operational management.

It is to be emphasized, however, that even the most proficient staff or consulting support cannot and should not supplant the strategic planning activities of senior management. These services can offer pertinent information and statistical data, invaluable analyses of alternative courses of action, and evaluations of the apparent strategic options; they should seldom present a *fait accompli* or a single recommended program with no reasonable alternative that seeks only the perfunctory approval of senior management. Whereas good staff work in the area of operations analysis is often mechanistic in nature and can commonly recommend one obviously superior solution to an identifiable and specific operating problem, staff and consulting support in the area of strategic analysis cannot submit crisp recommendations or final answers to senior management. The formulation of a strategy of manufacturing is not a task that can be delegated to either a staff or a consulting group; it is a task that must command the time, active participation, and best talents of the directors and senior officers of the organization with the staff and consulting groups fulfilling a supportive role. The scope and importance of manufacturing strategy precludes assigning primary responsibility for this managerial function to technological and analytical professionals only.

PARTICIPATION OF OPERATIONAL MANAGEMENT

Although strategy formulation is the province of senior management supported by the work of staff specialists and consultants, the contributions and limited participation of operational management are most desirable. Of the several ways this relationship can be developed, the establishment of the proper managerial environment is essential. Operational managers are to be sought and fostered who demonstrate strategic imagination and objectivity; without sacrificing managerial control of ongoing operations, these men are to be encouraged to view their operations as well as the organization's total activities strategically. Senior management is charged with constructing a managerial environment that stimulates change, foments new ideas, and honors originality and innovation. Lacking a salubrious climate, operational management not only fails to contribute invaluable inputs to the development of a manufacturing strategy but also fails to grow toward ultimately assuming the broader responsibilities of senior management.

It is revealing to note that recent research in cardinal utility theory—although preliminary and quite tentative—indicates that operational management displays an unquestionable bias against undertaking any course of action with a probability of culminating in a loss. Utility functions constructed from field investigations consistently display an aversion to even a modest probability of a loss, although the proposal's net probability may suggest an attractive return. Operational managers, for example, generally tend not to recommend a course of action offering a probability of 0.50 of either securing a gain of $400,000 or a loss of $75,000, even though the net probability of the proposal's outcome is quite attractive. The result of this type of behavior on the part of operational management is that excellent strategic proposals that happen to embody some probability of failure are never presented to senior management for consideration. To be credible, a managerial environment fostering new ideas and change must also accept as a corollary the probability of failure. An environment that is intolerant of failure will discourage new ideas, change, and purposeful risk taking; it assures that operational management will advance only the most conservative, risk-free, and uninspired proposals for consideration in developing a strategy of manufacturing.

The creative individual or organization can never accept the status quo complacently; is intellectually restless, impatient, and energetic; and views current problems or deficiencies not with annoyance, frustration, or dejection but as transient obstacles that will be overcome. Creativity is an exercise in optimism, a belief that there is a solution to even the most elusive problem, a conviction that there is a better way of doing any job, an acceptance of setbacks and periodic failure as the inevitable toll along the route to every worthwhile achievement, and a rejection of any performance not characterized by excellence and pre-eminence. By its very nature, creativity disrupts organizational harmony; it always introduces change, and change always menaces the organizational structure and the relationship of individuals and activities within the organization. However, creativity is a basic prerequisite of survival as well as growth; the organization failing to encourage, control, and implement individual creativity is pursuing a course toward extinction. Rather than suppressing creativity as a nuisance and a disruptive influence, the management of a viable organization will strive to design an organizational structure capable of accepting continual change and realignment, to maintain a climate in which questions and unconventional ideas are encouraged and expected, and to establish a rapport in which imaginative risk taking is not thwarted by the fear of possible failure.

Although it is laudable to state that senior management must establish a managerial climate that encourages new ideas and change, that fosters imagination and creativity, this type of environment is rarely realized without careful preparation and continuous cultivation. Prerequisites are the proper attitudes and intentions on the part of senior management; yet these attitudes and intentions are usually ineffectual without clear channels of strategic communications and responsive organizational relationships. Thus, in addition to processing industrial intelligence data and the various inputs from staff and consulting specialists, the strategic information system must be capable of processing a variety of inputs from operational management as well as the outputs, including directives, from senior management.

In most larger organizations, the desire to achieve an open and continuous dialogue between senior management and operational management in formulating a strategy of manufacturing is fatuous. First, considerations of industrial security and confidence often demand that many critical aspects of strategic planning be undertaken circumspectly with the participation of the smallest possible number of senior managers. Second, operational managers cannot be expected to devote the requisite time, investigation, and reflection to strategic planning without neglecting their operational responsibilities. And third, operational management rarely has routine access to and need for the full range of information upon which strategic planning must be founded. Consequently, the ways in which operational management is to contribute and participate in the formulation of a manufacturing strategy must be defined in each case with precision.

STRATEGIC PLANNING AND SITUATIONAL REPORTS

One of the ways in which operational management can constructively participate in the formulation of strategy is through the periodic issuance and subsequent discussion of strategic planning and situational reports. These reports—perhaps issued quarterly or semi-annually—seek to define and update with all possible specificity and candor within the limits of industrial security the manufacturing objectives, competitive environment, technological and market forecasts, resource requirements and commitments, and step-by-step program of action to implement the strategic plan. These strategic planning and situational reports in each functional area are the materials periodically bringing the unstructured work of staff and consulting groups into focus for review, evaluation, revision, and eventual implementation. They provide a concise statement of the strategy and directives of the directors (senior management); and, occasionally edited to delete sensitive points of industrial security, they provide essential planning and control criteria—that is, a sense of direction and acceleration—to operational management.

These strategic planning and situational reports must translate strategic directives into action commitments. Explicit statements must be made concerning what operational actions are to be taken, when, who is to be responsible, what resources are required, and how these resources are to be acquired. While these directives are not to devolve into operational planning, they are to establish quantitatively the objectives to be met and the actions to be taken by operational management. They are to specify the ways in which senior management is to be apprised of the conformance of operations to these strategic directives. Most of the required operational reports and performance feedback will be collected and transmitted through the operational information system; however, the type of strategic information, the points at which it is to be generated, and the ways in which it is to be transmitted to senior management are to be defined in the strategic planning and situational reports. Thus strategic directives are not only statements of intentions and objectives but specifications of the ways in which the strategy is to be enacted as well as the ways and standards by which operational conformance with these directives is to be monitored and evaluated.

In many cases, the desired dialogue between senior management and operational management is established by conducting strategic briefing sessions shortly after the issuance of these reports. Even though authoritative, these reports are to be issued frequently and early enough to elicit constructive response and feedback from operational management. Strategic briefing sessions are a primary two-way channel of communication in a strategic information system. They provide a means for senior management to communicate not only strategic directives but also the implications of the strategic decisions and the reasoning that has led to the selected course of action in contrast to alternative strategies. Although staff and consulting work must be based upon adequate contact with operational management in developing the initial information for strategy formulation, these strategic briefing sessions also seek the contributions and participation of operational management to confirm the soundness and likelihood of success of the operational aspects of the strategy, to refine appropriate features of the strategy to insure enhanced effectiveness, and through full understanding to enlist enthusiastic and unequivocal support in the vigorous execution of the strategy.

Several purposes are met through these strategic planning and situational reports, especially when amplified through subsequent strategic briefing sessions:

· The reports become internal planning documents of the highest importance, serving not only to enunciate the strategic directives of senior management but also as a medium of communication between various functional activities as well as between various levels of management.

· An explicit statement is constructed of the resources required to implement manufacturing strategy; the ways and schedule by which these resources are to be acquired and deployed are an essential part of this statement.

· Through a full comprehension of the enterprise's strategic objectives and program of action, operational management is offered quantitative guidelines for proximate planning and control. This knowledge can avoid the pursuit of operational programs that are in conflict with the manufacturing strategy of the organization.

· Rather than rhetorically asking for ideas and receiving a random selection of strategic proposals that are seldom in harmony with the objectives of senior management, these strategic planning and situational reports and the strategic briefing sessions offer operational management an adequately structured environment in which its contributions and participation can be expected to be especially fruitful.

MANUFACTURING APPRAISAL REPORTS

Manufacturing appraisal reports can be an important element of a strategic information system and can complement the strategic planning and situational reports in many ways. They are to be prepared by or in close cooperation with operational management and with the same frequency, but not at the same time, as the strategic planning and situational reports. The manufacturing appraisal reports will inform senior management of existing, excess, and programmed manufacturing capacity and capabilities; the ways in which productive capacity and capabilities are to be utilized is to be summarized, including a review of the analyses supporting the rejection of alternative uses. New product ideas that manufacturing management believes to be meritorious can be presented through these reports; whenever possible, these new product proposals should be evaluated quantitatively and accompanied with adequate *pro forma* data to enable market analyses to be undertaken with validity. Their exposure and interest usually place manufacturing management in a unique position to observe new technological developments and to apprise senior management of new manufacturing capabilities. Manufacturing appraisal reports can specify the ways in which these new technological developments and manufacturing capabilities are either to be acquired or to be exploited most profitably.

The manufacturing appraisal reports will tabulate planning and control criteria being employed for current and near-term operations; this discussion should reveal whether there is any conflict between these operational criteria and the strategic expectations of the organization. Similarly, an analysis of current manufacturing operations that are failing to meet profit, volume, or quality projections or other strategic objectives should be accompanied with specific programs of corrective action including resource requirements, time schedules, and interim performance standards. Manufacturing management is also in a privileged position to evaluate present product lines and to inform senior management of the ways in which certain product lines may warrant revision, redefinition or, possibly, abandonment. The periodic re-examination of existing product lines is an operational task with extensive strategic implications.

Finally, manufacturing appraisal reports are the communications medium for operational management to contribute directly and participate in the formulation of manufacturing strategy. They can proffer strategic objectives for consideration by senior management and pose questions of manufacturing strategy that appear to require clarification and definitive direction. They can provide essential feedback to the strategic planning and situational reports, particularly by identifying supplementary resource requirements and inaccurate statements of existing manufacturing capabilities. They can detect conflicts arising unwittingly through strategy revisions that may impose unanticipated burdens on manufacturing operations, and expose incongruities only readily apparent to operational management. Thus manufacturing appraisal reports are an essential component of a responsive strategic information system.

Several purposes may be met by manufacturing appraisal reports. They can provide a positive way to encourage manufacturing management to develop a balanced sense of self-awareness, to perceive objectively the strengths and weaknesses of present and contemplated operations. In this way, these reports can instill in manufacturing management an awareness of manufacturing strategy and a capability to think and plan strategically. Manufacturing appraisal reports offer orderly channels through which manufacturing management can present suggestions, new ideas, and specific information to senior management for consideration and possible incorporation into the strategic plan. This mode of communication provides a closed-loop control circuit permitting senior management to determine how well operational management understands the stated manufacturing strategy and is adapting current operations to its implications. Senior executive development and strategic information for superior manufacturing planning and control are the two broad advantages of manufacturing appraisal reports.

Thus the formulation and effective enactment of a manufacturing strategy is primarily dependent upon:

- The clear definition of who is responsible for strategy formulation.
- The design and utilization of a responsive strategic information system.
- The establishment of adequate organizational relationships to produce a constructive dialogue between operational and senior management.
- The formal and periodic pronouncement and dissemination by senior management of the manufacturing strategy and implementational plans of the enterprise.

SIGNIFICANCE OF SCALE OF OPERATIONS

Obviously, the suggested communications techniques may be unduly burdensome and unwieldy for a smaller organization. Although presented only as an illustration of one workable method of communications, the use of strategic planning and situational reports, strategic briefing sessions, and manufacturing appraisal reports requires a large investment of management, staff, and consulting time that is warranted in the large organization where manufacturing operations and strategy formulation involve extensive and complex interrelationships. Much of this paperwork may be simplified in the smaller organization, often with an improvement in coordination and communications. Yet, even in the smallest manufacturing organization, it is invariably desirable to insist upon some formality in strategy formulation and periodically to commit the approved manufacturing strategy to paper. Although every effort should be made to streamline the mechanics of planning regardless of the scale of operations, the basic strategic planning process is affected very little by the size of the organization.

Communications and the formulation and enactment of a manufacturing strategy become more complex for an organization employing a divisional or corporate group structure as opposed to a functional structure. The general manager of each division fulfills some aspects of the role of senior management, and certain elements of the strategic planning process may be undertaken by each division. However, the strategy of manufacturing is influenced not only by the objectives of the division's general management but also more strongly by the goals and active participation of headquarters staff and senior management. Division management in even the largest organizations is charged primarily with operational rather than strategic responsibilities; this emphasis is exemplified through the composition of the divisional staffs, the relatively short periods for which a division manager is appointed—two- to four-year periods being most common—and the gauging of managerial achievement largely by operating performance rather than by strategic improvement. Consequently, the strategic information system must embody channels of communications interconnecting senior management, headquarters manufacturing staff, division general management, division manufacturing management, and division staff. Although manufacturing strategy ultimately emanates from senior management, the exposure and competence of divisional management can result in exceptional contributions. In the largest industrial enterprises where divisions are organized into several corporate groups, the group executives may frequently fulfill most of the strategy formulation functions of senior management for their divisions. The strategic information system in the divisional organization must be designed with imagination to facilitate both the constructive participation of division management and the strategic direction of senior management.

The strategic planning and communications techniques employed by Raytheon Company have demonstrated dramatic results. At the end of 1964, the five-year strategic objectives of the corporation were forecast in summary as doubling sales volume, tripling total earnings, doubling earnings per share, and achieving an approximately equal balance between commercial sales and government sales volume by 1969. An aggressive program of commercial acquisitions is an important dimension of the strategic plan; this aspect of the program has been undertaken almost exclusively by senior management and had yielded six healthy commercial acquisitions by mid-1967.

However, in a manufacturing enterprise founded upon superiority in advanced technology, senior management emphasizes the crucial role of operational and divisional management in the formulation of manufacturing strategy for ongoing operations. While Raytheon's terminology is not identical, the corporation's strategic planning and communications process employs strategic planning and situational reports, in-depth strategic briefing sessions, and manufacturing appraisal reports. These activities generate explicit quantitative statements of the proximate and longer-range manufacturing objectives to be secured, the technological proficiencies to be acquired, the manufacturing resources to be employed, the interim performance standards to be met, and the operational monitoring, control and evaluation systems to be utilized. Application of these action-oriented strategic planning and control techniques resulted in increases for 1966 over 1965 in sales volume of 45 percent ($709 million versus $487.8 million), in total earnings of 67 percent ($18.4 million versus $11 million), in backlog of United States government work of 34 percent ($355 million versus $265 million), and in commercial sales volume (34 percent of total volume versus 17 percent of total volume). At the end of only the first two years of the five-year program, the corporation had achieved 56 percent of its sales volume objective, 62 percent of its total earnings objective, 48 percent of its earnings per share objective, and 54 percent of its commercial/government sales volume mix objective.

RESOURCE MANAGEMENT

Manufacturing strategy is concerned with the definition of manufacturing objectives and with the acquisition, development, deployment, and utilization of the manufacturing resources of the enterprise. Although it may be most pronounced in a divisional organization, senior management most commonly exercises strategic control through the capital budgeting process. It is not unusual for all requests for capital expenditures in excess of $250,000 to require the review and approval of the board of directors even in large manufacturing organizations; frequently, the procedures for requesting, approving, and controlling capital expenditures form the primary mode of the strategic information system.

Among the several weaknesses that can be harbored by this type of financial control, two deserve special attention. First, it gives unbalanced emphasis to senior management's control responsibilities and very little emphasis to its creative planning and leadership obligations; in actuality, strategic planning is being undertaken in a diffuse way by operational management and is being defined imperfectly through intermittent requests for capital funds. And second, although adequate procedures for evaluating and approving proposed capital investments are essential, in many organizations these procedures are so burdensome and sluggish that operational management may be discouraged from presenting the more imaginative and controversial proposals. This deficiency can be attributed partially to using the same channels of communication for both operational proposals and strategic proposals.

These weaknesses reveal that the capital budgeting process plans and controls only one type of manufacturing resource—money. A superior manufacturing strategy plans and controls all the resources of manufacturing—for example, the improvement and development of management and skilled personnel, manufacturing capabilities, advanced technological proficiencies, new products, and support of other functional activities.

A superior strategic budgeting process is employed by Olin Mathieson Chemical Corporation. While annual control budgets to program revenues and disbursements for the next year are an important operational control tool, senior management's primary attention is directed toward the five-year strategic capital allocation plan. This five-year capital budgeting plan is developed by senior management; it establishes a firm capital expenditures program for the next two years and guideline allocations for the subsequent three years. These strategic budgets are updated each year and, as FY-3 becomes FY-2, the guideline allocations are reviewed and transformed into a firm schedule of capital expenditures, while guideline allocations for the new FY-5 are incorporated into the next five-year capital budgeting plan. A critical part of this strategic budgeting process is the preparation of economic outlook reports by Olin's senior economist; these economic outlook reports introduce the significant external factors influencing the final statement of strategy.

The five-year strategic capital allocation plan, established by senior management, defines the direction, purpose, and strategy of the enterprise and is essentially a strategic planning and situational report. Adhering to these strategic criteria, the detailed development of budgeting data then originates at each profit center; these planning activities are next coordinated into five-year divisional plans supported by pro forma income statements by product line, cash flow schedules, balance sheets, analyses of both favorable and unfavorable profit changes, capital expenditures schedules by project, and evaluations of return on sales and net worth in comparison with competitors. The five-year divisional plans identify divisional objectives, the resources required or requested to meet these objectives, and significant manufacturing or marketing factors influencing the strategic criteria of the corporation; thus the dialogue established in the preparation of these divisional plans becomes the strategic appraisal reports of operational management.

Olin's senior management recognizes its obligation to provide forceful strategic leadership and direction as well as to maintain a responsive strategic information system permitting the constructive participation of operational management in the strategic planning process. Employing total assets in excess of $1.0 billion and with an annual capital investment program ranging between $75 million and $100 million, Olin focuses manufacturing strategy upon achieving the competitive initiative rather than reacting to competition in each of the varied industries in which it operates and upon continuing to improve its return on total assets as well as shareholder equity. The five-year strategic capital allocation plan—complemented by annual control budgets—is its primary management tool to achieve these strategic objectives.

STRATEGIC MANAGEMENT

The creative role of senior management is exercised not through the right of veto but through leadership, inspiration, and motivation. The viable manufacturing organization constructs a superior manufacturing strategy to achieve organizational leadership in some carefully defined area and to inspire and motivate operational management to enact this manufacturing strategy effectively. While strategy formulation employs the techniques of systems analysis and systems planning, the system must often be defined as encompassing much of the socio-economic environment in which the manufacturer exists. An inaccurate or even imprecise definition of the total system and of the function and objectives of the manufacturing organization within the total system constitutes a grievous miscarriage of senior management responsibilities. Senior management is consciously and continuously engaged in clarifying the definition of strategic (and consequently operational) objectives and must seek, evaluate, and select in broad and deliberate ways manufacturing objectives toward which the resources and energies of the enterprise are to be directed.

Once the manufacturing objectives of the organization have been defined with vision and promulgated with authority, it is possible to undertake an advance evaluation of the alternative means of securing these objectives. This is an activity where the participation of operational management can be especially constructive. Given a responsive strategic information system, a dialogue with operational management can be invaluable in the selection of superior near-term courses of action to achieve the strategic manufacturing objectives enunciated by senior management. It is invariably essential to establish interim objectives and to monitor progress toward these interim goals through the strategic information system. It is imperative that these interim goals be responsive to changes in organization values and strategic objectives due to the continual evolution and redefinition of manufacturing strategy; it is equally imperative that progress toward these interim goals be measured with speed and candor.

The multidimensional nature of strategy is expressed in terms of time, geography, function, and activity. Techniques of analysis now available permit the interaction of these various dimensions to be predicted with realism. In many cases, the combined effect of several dimensions or courses of action will be synergistic; in other cases, these interactions may partially cancel the efficacy of a course of action or result in other undesired consequences. Simulation techniques can stimulate the dialogue between senior management and operational management and—avoiding artificial oversimplifications —are often an enlightening way to cope with strategic multidimensional characteristics. Through the communications medium of simulation, it is possible to refine manufacturing strategy to minimize undesired consequences or to initiate supplemental courses of action to eliminate or compensate for these consequences.

The formulation of an imaginative strategy of manufacturing demands an intellectual rigor that, in the past, was not necessarily an attribute of senior management. Today, the potentialities of the management sciences, extensive communications, and specialized knowledge in virtually every area of industrial activity raise the magnitude of both the probable gains to be achieved through effective strategic planning and the losses, perhaps to the point of extinction, to be incurred due to the superior strategies of competitors. The formulation and enactment of a strategy of manufacturing are not the result of genial discussions or the part-time attention of senior management; it is formulated through strenuous intellectual efforts and enacted through full information, perceptive forecasts, and persuasive communication. Senior management secures the enthusiasm and unsparing support of operational management not through the exercise of its coercive authority but through the rigor of its logic, the inspiration of its vision, and the inevitability of its planning.

Reflections

If we could first know where we are and whither we are tending, we could better judge what to do and how to do it.

—Abraham Lincoln

I don't like to lose, and that isn't so much because it is just a football game, but because defeat means the failure to reach your objective. I don't want a football player who doesn't take defeat to heart, who laughs it off with the thought, "Oh, well, there's another Saturday."

—Knute Rockne

GROWTH IS A PHENOMENON of life, a requisite of vitality. Growth is one of the most fundamental manifestations of life; the absence of growth is a sign of morbidity and decay. Growth can be perceived in many ways other than increasing size. The life cycle of man offers an imperfect but still useful analogy. After the first quarter of a man's life, very little purposeful physical growth or size increase can be perceived; nevertheless, many kinds of critical growth—increasing skill, understanding, wisdom and judgment—can be observed for almost all of the duration of the life of a healthy man. Reproduction and the education and development of the young are still other ways in which man exhibits growth. In fact, it is significant to note that the healthy organism displays several kinds of growth. The uninterrupted dominance of only one mode of growth can lead to grotesqueness and rapid extinction. Only when similarly balanced patterns of growth are evident will the manufacturing organism possess vitality.

Change is a constant of nature. In all social and economic activities, change is the only certainty. But, although growth is invariably generated from within an organization, change can be both imposed by external factors and generated within an organization. Too often, it is assumed that change is an external phenomenon upon which the organization can exercise little influence; this passive or defensive attitude can draw the manufacturer toward the untenable position of reacting or adapting only to external change; that is, responding to the strategic initiative seized by competitors. Although it is essential to observe and compensate for change introduced by competitors, this is simply the defensive facet of a strategy of manufacturing. Creative change is one of manufacturing's most potent strategic resources; an aggressive strategy of manufacturing will purposefully create change in the quest for one or more manufacturing/marketing positions where the enterprise can exercise competitive leadership and superiority. Rather than seeking ways in which change can be avoided or mollified, a strategy of manufacturing will continually search for ways in which the enterprise can be not the pliant recipient, but the forceful instrument of change.

A kinetic strategy of manufacturing—a strategy of growth and change—is an expression primarily of imagination and determination rather than of analysis. The careful employment of all appropriate quantitative techniques of analysis can be invaluable in exploring certain aspects of a contemplated strategy. But numerical analyses are limited in respect to the kinds of questions they can evaluate, and excessive reliance upon quantitative techniques of analysis may result in the atrophy of senior management's strategic vision and courage. Analysis seldom leads to creativity or conviction; it may result in a greater understanding of the implications and interaction of a certain set of assumptions, but quantitative analysis cannot perceive alternative objectives, evaluate the qualitative dimensions of optional courses of action, or impart a sense of direction and acceleration to the enterprise. Imagination and determination are the management talents impregnating a strategy of manufacturing with perception, coherence, and originality.

INDICATIVE TRENDS

Growth and change are not new factors; they have been the cause of all history and have been of immediate importance since the advent of the Industrial Revolution. Although considerable evidence suggests that certain types of growth may be proliferating and the rate of change accelerating, these phenomena are more changes of degree than changes of kind or substance. However, a number of significant trends have been occurring in manufacturing, and a recognition of these changes is warranted. Contemporary changes may be no more portentous than those encountered by industrial management in the past, but it must be acknowledged that the characteristics of change are always in a state of change.

Perhaps the most fundamental trend is that our former notions of mass production—actually achieved only in rare cases and most likely never valid—are now perceived as being outmoded and are no longer even useful aspirations. Today, enhanced consumer expectations, market communications, and competition result in fewer uninterrupted long production runs. The variety of products appears to increase every year, owing to more precise and aggressive marketing efforts. New products are introduced more often, leading to shorter product life cycles. These characteristics raise the importance of manufacturing research and product development efforts, which in turn may increase the frequency and magnitude of product changes. Improved manufacturer-consumer communications lead more frequently to product adaptations designed to meet special purposes and to consumer-designated product specifications or configurations. Despite the managerial simplicity and operational economies to be secured through the traditional kind of mass production, a viable strategy of manufacturing will commonly be founded upon increasing product variation and market fractionation, thereby diminishing the potential role of mass production.

An advantageous manufacturing/marketing position can often be secured through the capability to meet short production lead times and immediate delivery commitments. Distributors and consumers employing advanced methods of inventory management and control now expect the manufacturer to be both a responsive and responsible part of their total logistics system; in turn, the manufacturer who offers his distributors and consumers ways in which their cost of inventory, materials handling, and ordering-expediting can be minimized attains an important competitive advantage. Invariably, efforts to provide these logistic services leads the manufacturer to establish an improved inventory-production-distribution scheduling and control system; this capability makes it both possible and economical to accept shorter lead times, rapid delivery commitments, and consequently shorter production runs. It is interesting to note that, although the computer can fulfill only a limited role in the formulation of a strategy of manufacturing—usually through the use of simulation models—it plays a crucial role in the development and utilization of a logistics information system; commonly, an important objective of manufacturing strategy is the establishment of a logistics information system to provide the resources with which to meet desired shorter lead times and delivery schedules reliably and profitably.

Another manifestation of this changing trend is higher product quality/reliability in performance and appearance. This characteristic has been most pronounced in the manufacture of matériel for military and aerospace programs. An unmistakable trend has also developed in consumer goods markets for enhanced standards of quality and reliability. In many cases, traditional methods and facilities of manufacture and quality control are inadequate to cope with these new product specifications. Again, the former notions of mass production do not provide for the present-day standards of quality and reliability assurance that not infrequently culminate in a zero defects program.

New technologies in processes and materials, new competitive factors—including direct and effective competition from both foreign sources and nontraditional domestic sources—and new dimensions in equipment acquisition decisions are still other manifestations of the changing characteristics of change. The magnitude and deliberateness of both industrial and government research and development activities produce a profusion of advances in process and material technologies; only the most assiduous industrial intelligence effort can identify the sources from which significant developments may be forthcoming or can anticipate the ways in which these developments may offer attractive manufacturing opportunities. Similarly, a strategy of manufacturing must continually assess the vulnerability of the enterprise to traditional as well as to new kinds of competition; the capabilities of current communication and transportation systems place almost every manufacturer in at least a continental and often a global market where the most unlikely competitors may suddenly be faced. And finally, even the routine acquisition of production equipment may now demand strategic direction—for example, the obsolescence of a battery of $18,000 milling machines may suggest the installation of a numerically controlled milling-drilling-tapping unit costing a quarter of a million dollars; or instead of a conventional warehouse employing fork-lift trucks and pallet racks, a fully mechanized high-bay warehouse may be warranted for the storage, order assembling, and shipping of finished goods or even of raw materials. Each of these considerations reveal ways in which the characteristics of change are observed to be changing.

To acknowledge the importance and pervasiveness of change does little to exploit the opportunities it presents or to deflect the competitive hazards accompanying it. In many cases, ill-conceived efforts to cope aggressively with change lead to consequences more destructive than simply drifting and reacting compliantly to change imposed by the external environment. Many strategic plans focused upon exploiting change emphasize action rather than the acquisition of adequate insight into the subtle, complex, and often reverberant ways in which significant change is to be effected. To acknowledge the constancy of change is only to acknowledge a natural phenomenon; a thoughtful and continual investigation of the composition and implications of the phenomenon and the attendant structural realignments is imperative before the enterprise can either create change or amplify emerging change with maximum effectiveness and economy. A potent strategy of manufacturing is directed not toward a euphemistic acknowledgment of change but toward specifying precisely and unequivocally where, how, and why change can be created, the appropriate response and exploitation of external change, and the resources to be mobilized and programs to be enacted to secure these objectives.

It has been suggested that a kinetic strategy for growth and change will be founded upon the internal development or the external acquisition of the resources and capabilities required to achieve the manufacturing objectives of the enterprise. An erroneous implication may be drawn that manufacturing strategy is concerned primarily with additions and expansions to the manufacturing capabilities of the organization—that is, with growth expressed solely through increase in the size and number of manufacturing activities. An equally important, and generally neglected, aspect of manufacturing strategy is the purging of activities no longer in harmony with or contributing to the objectives of the enterprise. Failure to divest an organization of nonessential, parasitic, or even aberrant manufacturing activities is a common cause of corporate malaise. As the manufacturing character, aspirations, and objectives of an enterprise evolve and change, it is imperative—even though frequently painful—to subject each manufacturing activity continually to the pattern of questions previously posed and to direct dispassionately the divestiture of those activities that do not support the manufacturing strategy of the enterprise. Objectivity and courage are demanded to direct the divestiture of operations that may contribute an attractive profit but that no longer fulfill a manufacturing objective of the organization.

A classic case of purging was displayed by the piano manufacturing activities of Sears, Roebuck and Co. During the early years of the 20th century, Sears sold pianos through its mail order catalogues and owned three small piano manufacturing companies to support this sales volume; these three companies were eventually consolidated into one subsidiary—Winter Piano Company. During the 1920's, changing living and cultural patterns, coupled with the development of the phonograph, led to a severe decline in the market for pianos. Sears was then able to acquire on attractive terms most of the expiring piano manufacturers, many holding a name and history of local prominence. By the 1930's, the company had become one of the major manufacturers of pianos, the piano factories were among its most profitable manufacturing activities, and the process of miniaturization—allowing smaller rooms and apartments to accommodate the smaller pianos, such as the spinet, comfortably—promised new popularity and broader market demand. However, by this time the buyers had discontinued the sale of pianos through both the catalogue and the retail stores; all piano sales were being made through independent dealers requiring a separate sales organization and credit system. Although this manufacturing activity generated an excellent profit and offered attractive growth potential, it was no longer in harmony with the company's strategic manufacturing objective—to support the mass distribution of middle-income consumer merchandise through mail order catalogues and company retail stores. Thus, in 1938, Sears divested itself of its piano factories.

PROFIT ORIENTATION

To state that manufacturing strategy is to be profit-oriented may be little more than to utter the self-evident. Still, several kinds of profit contributions or potentialities that may be secured through a manufacturing activity are of sufficient variety and significance to warrant identification and summarization.

Deriving a manufacturing profit would appear to be an axiomatic objective calling for no further investigation. Innumerable cases can be cited where a manufacturing activity both supports a total corporate objective and earns a valid independent profit. Regrettably, in multidivisional organizations or in those cases where manufacturing is not the dominant functional activity, it is frequently quite difficult if not impossible to identify indisputably the profit contribution of manufacturing operations. Several basic considerations make it unlikely that the accounting profession can ever define one right way to establish equitable transfer prices, just as there is no way to calculate precisely a fair price for any commodity, product, or service; while always subject to criticism and occasional abuses—and excluding the special case of a publicly franchised or monopolistic position—the reasonably unrestricted interplay of market forces remains the least offensive method of establishing any price.

However, whenever manufacturing operations are supporting other organizational activities and are not in meaningful competition with external suppliers, the determination of transfer price schedules is inevitably based upon certain artificial calculations and arbitrary practices. In these cases, an evaluation of the real profit contribution of a manufacturing activity presents special problems; in most instances, these activities should be investigated periodically to ascertain as realistically as possible—often independently of routine accounting procedures—their actual profit contribution.

The generation of a manufacturing profit may be neither a manufacturing objective or expectation, nor a sufficient justification for retaining a manufacturing activity. Acknowledging the resource limitations faced by any organization, a strategy of manufacturing will constantly seek the maximum return on the total resources invested in the enterprise. This objective may be achieved most effectively by manufacturing activities that—although contributing very little, if any, profit to the organization—enable other corporate objectives to be realized with maximum efficacy and profitability. Two from among many possible examples of the production of certain so-called unprofitable products would be:

- Products that cannot be procured satisfactorily from external sources of supply to complete a desired product-market spectrum.
- Products that permit an advanced manufacturing proficiency to be developed to meet long-range corporate objectives.

Both objectives appear to be the rationale behind the reported losses incurred by some of General Electric Company's computer systems operations. The corporation's joint investment with Compagnie des Machines Bull of France resulted in a shared deficit of $23.3 million in 1966 and a loss of $50.7 million during the previous 18 months when substantial start-up and reorganization costs were incurred. In embarking upon the venture, General Electric anticipated this loss of current earnings, which was ascribed to major product and market development efforts coupled with technological and nationalistic conflicts arising from the integration of the computer lines of the two separate organizations. Anticipating the growth of the Western European computer market of 20 percent per year, in contrast to a current annual growth rate of 12 percent in the United States, General Electric agreed in May 1967 to invest an additional $30.2 million in the two major Bull operating subsidiaries—Societé Industrielle Bull–General Electric, a manufacturing organization, and Compagnie Bull–General Electric, a marketing organization—thereby raising its total investment in the enterprise to almost $100 million and increasing its equity participation from 50 percent to 66 percent. The corporation views its computer systems operations as an important future growth business and accepts these near-term losses as an investment in broadening a desired product-market spectrum requiring an internationally oriented advanced manufacturing proficiency.

Thus a profit-oriented evaluation of both contemplated and ongoing manufacturing activities will look beyond the manufacturing profit attributable to the specific operation and will assess the near-term and long-range incremental profit derived through the manufacturing activity. On the other hand, it has been emphasized that manufacturing activities that contribute real and attractive profits but do not fulfill the manufacturing objectives of the organization are to be made congruent with these objectives or are to be divested. (Occasionally the proper alternative is to redefine the strategy of manufacturing to encompass these apparently divergent operations.) The prolonged support of these peripheral manufacturing activities, even though they contribute a profit, can result in an imprudent diffusion of the physical, financial, and managerial resources of the enterprise, and in an irresolute deflection of effort and movement from the strategic objectives of manufacturing.

Seeking ways in which the organization's products can yield improved profits to the consumer is the most effective way of assuring improved profits to the manufacturing enterprise. Increased profits to the consumer through the acquisition and use of the product may be secured through:

- Improved earnings to the consumer; for example, heavy-duty trucks with performance characteristics that result in more profitable operations to an interstate common carrier.
- Demonstrably lower operating costs to the consumer; for example, a material-handling installation that results in substantial operating savings and an attractive return on investment.
- Improved service reliability to the consumer; for example, raw materials that are more uniform or dimensionally stable, result in less down time, fewer equipment and process adjustments, or higher throughput rates.
- Convenience, ease of operation, or what might be regarded as psychic profits to the consumer; for example, food products that are easier or faster to prepare, add exciting variety to a

family diet, or offer outstandingly appetizing taste, appearance, or quality.

The consumer purchases the manufacturer's products to obtain an advantage—a profit—presumably greater than that offered by the alternative purchasing opportunities available to him. A low initial cost is always one factor that suggests product profitability to the consumer; this consideration is frequently of secondary significance when matched against recognized and continuing operating advantages. Therefore, manufacturing strategy will be directed not only toward improving product profitability to the manufacturer but also—often of greater importance—toward enhancing its profitability to the consumer.

Profit orientation also demands that products offer superior profit opportunities to distributors. Manufacturing costs constitute only about 41 percent of the ultimate consumer price; distribution costs represent between one-fourth to one-half of every retail sales dollar. A product of outstanding design, a product with an unchallenged market position, or an unique product for which there is no adequate substitute may sell itself, thereby offering attractive profit opportunities to distributors. In other cases, the design of the product in conjunction with the way in which it is packaged, shipped, and handled may yield tangible material-handling economies to distributors; the ability to meet special orders and rapid delivery requests may lower inventory costs for distributors and enable them to provide superior customer service; improved product quality and reliability may result in enhanced customer satisfaction, fewer returns or adjustments, fewer service calls, and consequently greater product profitability to distributors. Competitive price and discount schedules are usually the primary method of assuring distributors of adequate product profitability. However, a strategy of manufacturing will be directed toward developing and accentuating the many product attributes and manufacturer services that will result in a superior profit contribution to distributors.

THE MECHANIZATION/FLEXIBILITY DILEMMA

Another fundamental trend that frequently appears to be in opposition to the diminishing importance of traditional mass production is the increasing mechanization or automation of manufacturing operations. This irreversible trend toward advanced mechanization is justified by—

· The continually changing balance between the costs of labor and capital equipment as wage costs increase unrelentingly while technological creativity and innovation lower the comparative costs of performing more and more formerly manual activities by electromechanical means.

· The impossibility of meeting many product specifications and marketing requirements with any technique of manufacture other than electromechanical equipment.

However, any presumed conflict between increasing mechanization and the decline of former notions of mass production may be due to an inaccurate recollection of mass production.

As manifested during the first half of the 20th century and illustrated most conspicuously by the automotive industry, the requisites of mass production were the interchangeability of standard components, the unprecedented specialization of labor, the mechanical movement of work from operation to operation—for example, the moving assembly line—rather than the movement of workers, and a very large volume of a limited variety of standard and only infrequently changing products. Although these requisites of mass production did demand some degree of mechanization, the degree of automaticity was usually low in comparison with the standards of mechanization that are now commonplace; in fact, the two unique advances embodied in mass production were the mechanical movement of work usually displaying the most rudimentary mechanization and the refined specialization of labor, revealing that most mass production operations were still labor intensive. Thus, although its managerial simplicity and unrivaled manufacturing economies make mass production an objective to be pursued whenever feasible, it is important to recognize that mass production and a high level of mechanization in manufacturing are not synonymous.

The unceasing mechanization of manufacturing operations is to be directed toward reducing the labor content of each unit of production as well as improving both the product and service of the manufacturer. While mechanization always strives to minimize the total unit costs of production, it is often of greater importance to mechanize a manufacturing operation to achieve greater flexibility, expanded product variety, shorter changeover times, and higher quality/reliability standards. Obviously, electromechanical operations fulfilling these objectives exhibit outstanding engineering vision and design ingenuity. No mechanical operation can ever incorporate the skilled human operatives' potential range of capabilities; nevertheless, taking into account the scarcity of skilled operatives in any labor force and the high cost of having these skilled individuals continually learning new jobs or new methods of performing old jobs, it is quite possible to mechanize many operations in ways that can accommodate growth and change more satisfactorily than human operatives.

In an expanding number of cases, numerical control and computer-directed operations may offer one solution to the mechanization/flexibility dilemma. Numerically controlled equipment can often be designed and subsequently programmed to perform a much broader range of operations than would be performed by standard equipment tended by human operatives. Computer direction of manufacturing operations and processes usually achieves a similar multiple of performance capabilities and flexibility in contrast to the traditional techniques of production line and process direction and control. These technologies and several specialized variants of these technologies frequently enable a high degree of mechanization to be achieved without the former concomitant of restrictive inflexibility.

Even a small manufacturer may formulate an effective strategy founded upon numerical control or computer-directed operations. The Overly Manufacturing Company, a manufacturer of industrial, institutional, and commercial metal doors and frames, with a 145-man plant, faced production scheduling deficiencies caused by varying customer specifications that led to small production runs—as few as six doors per run. Variations include locations on the door for windows, louvers, peepholes, and hardware—which also varied by type and vendor—metal skins varying in gauge and type, and 92 different door patterns. Following an investigation initiated in 1959, it was determined that a numerically controlled press to punch the virtually unlimited number of possible standard and special hole combinations in the door skins, instead of punching from a scribed layout or template, was an essential installation before a computer-directed production control system could achieve maximum effectiveness. This equipment was installed in 1964.

Now, after originating a programming form, the computer center produces a production schedule, shearing and bending instructions, and an N/C tape; multiple-part labels (including a shipping identity label) are emitted for production control to identify each of the door skins and any subassemblies making up a door assembly. Computer programs generate a detailed bill of materials that tabulates part numbers by cut length; these components are the reinforcements, moldings, channels, louvers and glass light subassemblies for installation in the cut holes described by the N/C program. This $200,000 installation has resulted in a substantial reduction in operatives, the elimination of nine units of equipment, a major compression in production cycle time for door panels, a reduction in rework, and a notable improvement in meeting delivery schedules. Most significantly, this numerically controlled equipment and computer-directed production control system has transformed a large job shop into a production-line operation that can accommodate broad variations in product characteristics and configurations while maintaining flexibility, reliability, and a profitable price structure that is still competitive with other manufacturers in the industry.

It is to be noted, however, that the inherent flexibility of numerical control and computer-directed operations cannot be expected to result in the "universal machine" within the foreseeable future. Although vastly expanded capabilities can be realized, these advanced electromechanical manufacturing facilities can only perform the specific operations envisioned in establishing the initial design criteria. Economic feasibility inevitably requires design criteria to be confined within much narrower limits than those that are technologically feasible. It is also noteworthy that these types of mechanization are usually embodied in only one or a few critical production operations and can rarely encompass a total manufacturing system; although it remains especially difficult to realize a high level of mechanization in assembly operations, significant achievements in automaticity are being realized in the increasingly important and formerly labor-intensive operations of product testing and quality assurance. Thus the manufacturing technologies of numerical control and computer direction may enable high levels of mechanization and flexibility to be attained, but these developments are no panacea for myopia in establishing design criteria; capital investments for these advanced installations, because they are of an order of magnitude appreciably higher than those experienced even in the recent past, demand that design criteria be specified with prudence and vision.

Imaginative product design offers other ways in which flexibility may be combined with manufacturing operations that display a high level of mechanization. Modular design and interchangeable optional components often allow several models of a product and many variations of the same product to be run over the same production line. The permutations and combinations of product design characterized by these features can result in broad variations of product configuration and performance and simultaneously can be capable of manufacture by highly mechanized operations. However, the automotive industry—a popular case during the past decade of a proliferation of models, propulsion alternatives, trim and finish combinations, and customer-designated options—illustrates the limitations of product design. Every effort appears to have been exerted to utilize modular design and interchangeable optional components, and continual improvement can be observed in the mechanization, and even in the automation, of parts and components production; nevertheless, aside from the ingenuity evidenced in material handling and power-assisted hand tools, automobile assembly is not characterized by a high level of mechanization and is still a comparatively labor-intensive activity. Increasingly complex markets, demanding greater variations and individuality in mass-produced products, cause the promise 50 years ago of mass production to culminate in the automatic factory to remain unfulfilled.

VERTICAL INTEGRATION

A manufacturing strategy is to be polarized forward toward the market rather than backward toward traditional raw materials. It may be trite to note that a manufacturing operation is established primarily, not to transform certain raw materials into more finished products, but to create and then satisfy the needs or demands of selected markets. However, despite the constantly increasing number of market-oriented enterprises, managements assuming this stance often fail to perceive the implications to manufacturing operations. To be meaningful, a strategy of manufacturing must be carefully coordinated and in total harmony with the marketing strategy of the organization. On the other hand, a marketing strategy is invariably devoid of substance until it is energized by a responsive strategy of manufacturing.

If a manufacturing strategy is to be market-oriented rather than polarized toward traditional raw materials, does this suggest that basic manufacturers should integrate forward to develop captive or controlled markets, or that large merchandisers should integrate backward to acquire in-house manufacturing capabilities? Although this type of vertical integration has been occurring for almost a century, it is precarious to claim that any dominant trend is present. Cases of manufacturers integrating forward to the ultimate market are often observed, but it has been considerably more common for mass merchandisers to integrate backward into manufacturing. Yet successful backward integration by merchandisers seldom results in establishing a broad manufacturing capability; it is commonly directed toward securing only limited and carefully selected manufacturing objectives.

Most of the larger grocery chains operate their own bakeries, fluid milk plants, and certain other food-processing facilities. In each case, the products being manufactured usually are undifferentiated commodities rather than unique proprietary products for which a strong consumer franchise has been established, the manufacturing technology is not highly complex, and the merchandiser will generally continue to carry the branded products of independent manufacturers to complement the private label merchandise. It should also be recognized that the two most common manufacturing activities of the grocery chains—bakeries and fluid milk plants—enjoy vested advantages because of certain unrealistic distribution costs and price schedules imposed upon independent wholesale bakeries and milk processors. Although Sears, Roebuck and Co. is engaged in a multitude of manufacturing activities, it has never sought to manufacture the majority of its merchandise. A mass merchandiser's strategy of manufacturing must be formulated with particular care to define the specific objectives to be achieved.

In addition to the various objectives already discussed, certain limited manufacturing capabilities are often maintained by merchandising organizations primarily as a powerful component of purchasing strategy. Cases can be cited of numerous mass merchandisers who have been unable to conclude satisfactory procurement contracts with established manufacturers for certain important product groups they believe to be necessary for inclusion in their merchandising spectrum. In these cases, the merchandising organization may develop its own facilities to design and produce these products. Although these manufacturing operations may not generate significant earnings, they can achieve their primary objective of enabling the merchandiser to offer the desired product group and eventually to compel the independent manufacturers to enter into acceptable procurement contracts; once these objectives are secured, the manufacture of its own products can be discontinued.

A new 1,500,000 square foot ($30 million) food-processing and -manufacturing plant at Horseheads, New York, was placed in operation in 1965 by The Great Atlantic & Pacific Tea Company, Inc. (A&P). This extensive facility was established to secure improved manufacturing profits and quality standards by consolidating several small older operations and by employing the most advanced and economical processing equipment. However, the logistical advantage of making direct shipments of processed foods as well as other merchandise throughout the eastern part of the United States is one of the most important operating economies offered by this new plant. Even if the real costs of manufacturing resulted in no significant advantage over former plant costs or the alternative procurement costs of comparable products, the distribution economies associated with the Horseheads facility would prove to be exceptionally attractive. Thus the investigation of a program of vertical integration demands an objective evaluation of the total manufacturing/distribution system.

The actual or potential threat of backward integration into manufacturing by mass merchandisers always poses questions of strategic significance to independent manufacturers. However, the manufacturer occupying manufacturing/marketing positions where competitive leadership and superiority can be exercised is comparatively invulnerable to this type of competition. Despite the manufacturing activities of the major grocery chains, all of these chains carry the products of the General Foods Corporation, Standard Brands Incorporated, General Mills, Inc., and the other major food processors; in many cases, these outstanding food processors enjoy profit positions equal or superior to those attained by their mass-merchandising customers. Today, Polaroid cameras, Corning Ware cookware, and

Gillette razor blades are sold by Sears, Roebuck and Co. Although the marginal manufacturer is always vulnerable to competition from every quarter, the manufacturer who attains a position of recognized superiority can invariably respond to competition aggressively and on his own terms.

The Symbiotic Option

A strategy of manufacturing may select a symbiotic relationship as the most effective route to a specified objective. In biological terms, *symbiosis* denotes two species of organism living together harmoniously in an association that is mutually advantageous or even essential to both. Certain research and development, manufacturing, and marketing objectives can only be achieved or can be achieved more efficiently by joining forces with other allies. One of the most mature symbiotic ventures is the Owens-Corning Fibreglas Corporation, an enterprise established jointly in the 1930's by the Corning Glass Works and Owens-Illinois, Inc. (formerly the Owens-Illinois Glass Company) to manufacture and market a new product utilizing fine-drawn glass filaments—Fibreglas—developed independently by each company. The SunOlin Chemical Company was established by the Sun Oil Company and the Olin Mathieson Chemical Corporation to combine the urea production that was made available by Sun Oil's excess ammonia capacity with Olin's need for urea in its fertilizer operations. The Penn-Olin Chemical Company (Olin Mathieson Chemical Corporation and the Pennsalt Chemicals Corporation), the Jefferson Chemical Company (Texaco Inc. and American Cyanamid Company), the Texas U.S. Chemical Company (Texaco Inc. and United States Rubber Company), Goodrich-Gulf Chemicals, Inc. (The B.F. Goodrich Company and Gulf Oil Corporation), and the Avisun Corporation (American Viscose Company and Sun Oil Company) are only a few of the better-known symbiotic associations. Relationships may take the form of subcontracts, franchises, licensing agreements, joint ventures, partnerships, or new businesses. These combinations, naturally, can be subject to antitrust action; in the Petroleum Chemicals case—a joint venture of the Cities Service Company and the Continental Oil Company—the combination was disallowed, and Cities Service sold its interest to the Continental Oil Company. However, the creation of a symbiotic relationship utilizing the complementary resources of two organizations can be an imaginative and forceful strategy of manufacturing.

BIFOCAL MANAGEMENT

Although certain distinctions between strategic planning and long-range planning have been emphasized, the distant planning horizons of each of these activities can be misconstrued to imply that they strive to fix in unnatural and frequently dangerous ways the future course of the manufacturing organization. It is often presumed that these activities are concerned with making future decisions and committing the organization to a series of future actions. These mistaken notions may be caused by semantics—joining the terms "planning" and either "long-range" or "strategic."

Industrial management should never attempt to make future strategic decisions. Although procrastination cannot be tolerated, a strategic decision is never to be made prematurely; it should always be postponed until it *has* to be made. In fact, a strategy of manufacturing is concerned with long-range thinking and near-term planning; it is concerned with the futurity of the decisions and actions that must be undertaken today. Manufacturing strategy is a definition of the near-term, long-range, and flexibility objectives of the enterprise, imparting a valid sense of direction and acceleration to the organization; it offers a frame of reference assuring that current and near-term decisions and actions are congruent and are undertaken in harmony with these manufacturing objectives.

These objectives are to be selected with care and vision but always tentatively and subject to reconsideration, redefinition, and—not infrequently—subsequent rejection. However, the thoughtful definition of the objectives of manufacturing simultaneously defines the purposeful ways in which the organization is now expected to grow, both to create change and to respond to change. A viable organization will not hesitate to change these objectives as the future presents new or unanticipated opportunities and as the external environment causes structural realignments within and between industries. A kinetic strategy of manufacturing for growth and change will itself be in a continual state of growth and change, of evolution. However, this healthy characteristic in no way detracts from the usefulness of manufacturing strategy as a guide by which superior current and near-term operational decisions can be made and enacted.

In the larger and most astute industrial enterprises, a strategy of manufacturing is commonly stated in certain formal planning documents promulgated by senior management. These planning documents are supported by thorough and continuing analyses of objectives, strategic opportunities, and optional courses of action. Nevertheless, while these analyses can explore and evaluate certain aspects and interrelationships of a contemplated course of action, the inherent uncertainties of manufacturing strategy preclude these analyses from formulating strategy or from presenting automatic decisions.

Although the most advanced quantitative techniques of analysis must always be employed to identify and structure the factors of uncertainty, management enthusiasm and resolution is the strategic factor that reduces and often eliminates uncertainty. Formal planning documents are the tools of communications and are essential to communicate with clarity and authority the long-range thinking and objectives of senior management to operational management. A kinetic strategy of manufacturing is the vision, courage, and precise thinking of senior management in the manufacturing enterprise.

Bibliography

Anderson, W. H. Locke. *Corporate Finance and Fixed Investment: An Econometric Study.* Boston: Division of Research, Graduate School of Business Administration, Harvard University, 1964.

Ansoff, H. Igor. *Corporate Strategy.* New York: McGraw-Hill Book Company, Inc., 1965.

Anthony, Robert N. *Planning and Control Systems: A Framework for Analysis.* Boston: Division of Research, Graduate School of Business Administration, Harvard University, 1965.

Barrish, Norman N. *Economic Analysis for Engineering and Managerial Decision-Making.* New York: McGraw-Hill Book Company, 1962.

Beyer, Robert. *Profitability Accounting for Planning and Control.* New York: The Ronald Press Company, 1963.

Branch, Melville C. *The Corporate Planning Process.* New York: American Management Association, Inc., 1962.

Bright, James R. *Automation and Management.* Boston: Division of Research, Graduate School of Business Administration, Harvard University, 1958.

———. *Research, Development, and Technological Innovation.* Homewood, Ill.: Richard D. Irwin, Inc., 1964.

Bursk, Edward C., and John F. Chapman (editors). *New Decision-Making Tools for Managers.* Cambridge, Mass.: Harvard University Press, 1963.

Chamberlain, Neil W. *The Firm: Micro-Economic Planning and Action.* New York: McGraw-Hill Book Company, 1962.

Chandler, Alfred D., Jr. *Strategy and Structure. Chapters in the History of the Industrial Enterprise.* Cambridge, Mass.: The M.I.T. Press, 1962.

Churchman, C. West, Russell L. Ackoff, and E. Leonard Arnoff. *Introduction to Operations Research.* New York: John Wiley & Sons, Inc., 1957.

Dean, Joel. *Capital Budgeting.* New York: Columbia University Press, 1951.

———. *Managerial Economics.* Englewood Cliffs, N.J.: Prentice-Hall, Inc., 1951.

Dearden, John. *Computers in Business Management.* Homewood, Ill.: Dow Jones-Irwin, Inc., 1966.

———. *Cost and Budget Analysis.* Englewood Cliffs, N.J.: Prentice-Hall, Inc., 1962.

Bibliography

DeSimone, Daniel V. (editor). *Technological Innovation: Its Environment and Management*. Washington, D.C.: U.S. Government Printing Office, 1967.

Dewing, Arthur Stone. *The Financial Policy of Corporations* (2 volumes). New York: The Ronald Press Company, 1953.

Diebold, John. *Beyond Automation*. New York: McGraw-Hill Book Company, Inc., 1964.

Ewing, David W. (editor). *Long-Range Planning for Management*. New York: Harper & Row, 1964.

Financial Executives Research Foundation, Inc. *Mergers and Acquisitions: Planning and Action*. New York: 1963.

Forrester, Jay W. *Industrial Dynamics*. Cambridge, Mass.: M.I.T. Press, 1961.

Goetz, Billy E. *Quantitative Methods: A Survey and Guide for Managers*. New York: McGraw-Hill Book Company, 1965.

Hackney, John W. *Control and Management of Capital Projects*. New York: John Wiley & Sons, Inc., 1965.

Hanssmann, Fred. *Operations Research in Production and Inventory Control*. New York: John Wiley & Sons, Inc., 1962.

Hunt, Pearson. *Financial Analysis in Capital Budgeting*. Boston: The Graduate School of Business Administration, Harvard University, 1964.

Johnson, Richard A., Fremont E. Kast, and James E. Rosenzweig. *The Theory and Management of Systems*. New York: McGraw-Hill Book Company, 1963.

Kast, Fremont E., and James E. Rosenzweig. *Science, Technology, and Management*. New York: McGraw-Hill Book Company, 1963.

Kepner, Charles H., and Benjamin B. Tregoe. *The Rational Manager: A Systematic Approach to Problem Solving and Decision Making*. New York: McGraw-Hill Book Company, 1965.

Leavitt, Theodore. *Innovation in Marketing: New Perspectives for Profit and Growth*. New York: McGraw-Hill Book Company, 1962.

LeBreton, Preston P., and Dale A. Henning. *Planning Theory*. Englewood Cliffs, N.J.: Prentice-Hall, Inc., 1961.

Mace, Myles L., and George G. Montgomery Jr. *Management Problems of Corporate Acquisitions*. Boston: Graduate School of Business Administration, Harvard University, 1962.

McCarthy, George D. *Acquisitions and Mergers*. New York: The Ronald Press Company, 1963.

Miller, Stanley S. *The Management Problems of Diversification*. New York: John Wiley & Sons, Inc., 1963.

Moore, Franklin G. *Manufacturing Management*. Homewood, Ill.: Richard D. Irwin, Inc., 1965.

Morris, William T. *The Analysis of Management Decisions*. Homewood, Ill.: Richard D. Irwin, Inc., 1964.

Optner, Stanford L. *Systems Analysis for Business Management*. Englewood Cliffs, N.J.: Prentice-Hall, Inc., 1960.

Paton, William A. *Corporate Profits: Measurement, Reporting, Distribution, Taxation*. Homewood, Ill.: Richard D. Irwin, Inc., 1965.

Bibliography

Rautenstrauch, Walter, and Raymond Villers. *The Economics of Industrial Management.* New York: Funk & Wagnalls Company, 1957.

Reichard, Robert S. *Practical Techniques of Sales Forecasting.* New York: McGraw-Hill Book Company, 1966.

Scharf, Charles A. *Techniques for Buying, Selling and Merging Businesses.* Englewood Cliffs, N.J.: Prentice-Hall, Inc., 1964.

Schmookler, Jacob. *Invention and Economic Growth.* Cambridge, Mass.: Harvard University Press, 1966.

Schon, Donald A. *Technology and Change: The New Heraclitus.* New York: Delacorte Press, 1967.

Scott, Brian W. *Long-Range Planning in American Industry.* New York: American Management Association, Inc., 1965.

Silberman, Charles E. *The Myths of Automation.* New York: Harper & Row, 1966.

Simon, Herbert A. *The New Science of Management Decision.* New York: Harper & Row, 1960.

Solomon, Ezra (editor). *The Management of Corporate Capital.* Glencoe, Ill.: The Free Press, 1959.

Spencer, Milton H., and Louis Siegelman. *Managerial Economics: Decision Making and Forward Planning.* Homewood, Ill.: Richard D. Irwin, Inc., 1964.

Steiner, George A. (editor). *Managerial Long-Range Planning.* New York: McGraw-Hill Book Company, 1963.

———. *Multinational Corporate Planning.* New York: The Macmillan Company, 1966.

Urwick, Lyndall F. *Leadership in the Twentieth Century.* London: Sir Isaac Pitman & Sons Ltd., 1957.

Withington, Frederic G. *The Use of Computers in Business Organizations.* Reading, Mass.: Addison-Wesley Publishing Company, 1966.

Index

Index

International Telephone and Telegraph Corporation, 64
Inventory, 169
  turnover of, 55–56

J

Jefferson Chemical Company, 182
Jones & Laughlin Steel Corporation, 43

K

Kanthal, 17
Kellwood Company, 22
Kent-Coffey Manufacturing Company, 122
Koppers Company, Inc., 45

L

Liquidity, 60
  "physical," 60–61, 134–135
Literacy, universal, 14
Litton Industries, Inc., 64
Logistics, 38–41, 132, 169, 181
Long-range planning, 68, 149, 183

M

McDonnell Company, 70–72
McLouth Steel Corporation, 43
Magnavox Company, 122
Manufacturing, definition and scope, 18–20
Manufacturing appraisal reports, 157–159
Market, enlargement of the scope of, 53
Market analysis, 141, 157
  functional versus technical, 87–88
Market development, 75–79, 109, 117
Market share, increase in, 53
Mass production, 168, 175–179
Material handling, 36, 121–122, 169, 174–175, 179
Maximin principle, 96
Metals markets, 16–17
Metro-Goldwyn-Mayer, Inc., 20
Micro-electronics, 81
Millom Hematite Ore & Iron Company, 44
Minimax principle, 96

Minimax regret principle (L. J. Savage), 96
Minnesota Mining & Manufacturing Company, 102–103
Models, use of, in formulating manufacturing strategy, 18, 96–98, 105–106, 114, 164–165, 169
Modular design, 179
Mohasco Industries, Inc., 122–123
Monsanto Company, 113
Motion picture industry, 20–21
Multi-industry form of organization, 63–64
Multimarket form of organization, 63–64

N

National Steel Corporation, 44–45
News media, 14
Numerical control, 35–36, 170, 177–179

O

Objectives, 86, 103–104, 106, 182
  corporate, 17, 27
  divergent, 48–49, 123–125
  flexibility, 49–50, 57–61, 63–65, 183
  long-range, 49, 52–57, 63–65, 69, 183
  manufacturing, 47–65, 72–73, 164, 174, 183
  near-term, 49–53, 63–65, 69, 183
  peripheral, 61–65
Obsolescence, 17–18, 134
  technological, 74
Office equipment industry, 116
Olin Mathieson Chemical Corporation, 57, 162–163, 182
Organism, manufacturing as an, 107–125
Overly Manufacturing Company, 177–178
Owens-Corning Fibreglas Corporation, 182
Owens-Illinois, Inc., 182

P

Packaging, 19, 21, 175
Paper Mate Division (The Gillette Company), 33